Marguerite Brennan.
A present from Butlins
from Carmel. 1982.

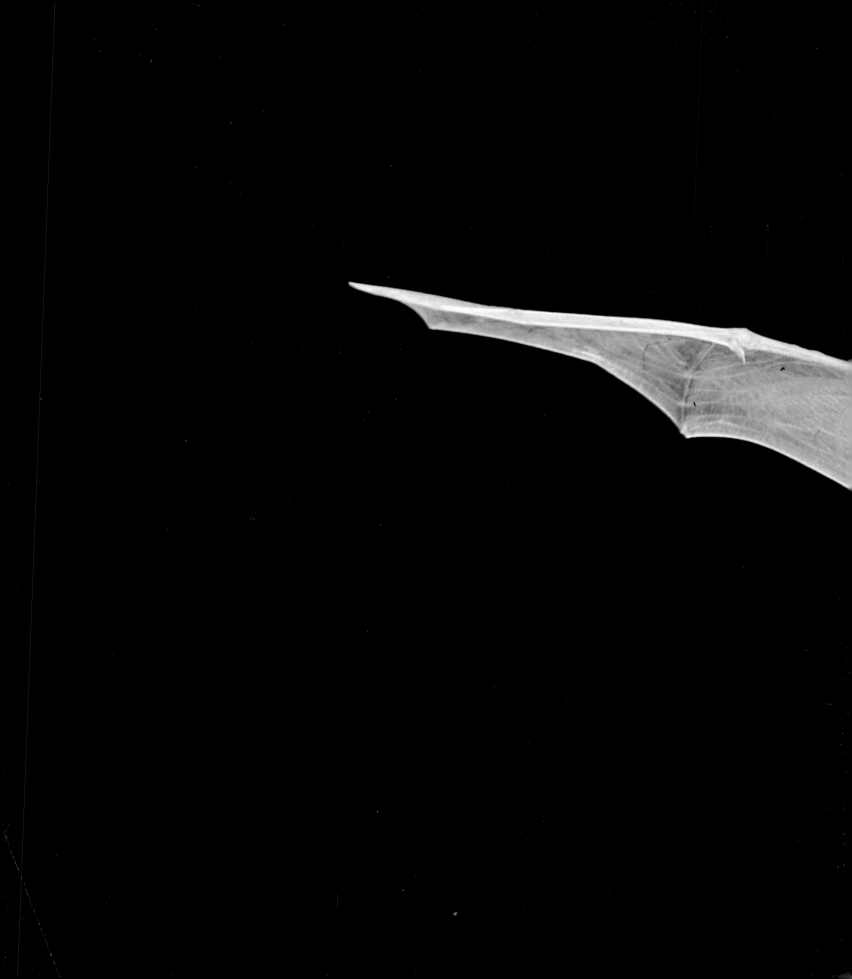

The Illustrated
Encyclopedia of the *Animal*
Kingdom

The Danbury Press

Editorial direction and supervision for the English language edition by PERCY KNAUTH.

Associate Editor—DALE MCADOO.

Art direction and design by JACK JAGET.

Volume 6—Adapted by PAUL JENSEN

The Danbury Press, a division of Grolier Enterprises, Inc.
    Publisher—ROBERT B. CLARKE.
    Marketing Director—ROBERT G. BARTNER.
    Creative Director—GILBERT EVANS.
    Publishing Consultant—DAVID MENDELSOHN.
    Assistant to the Publisher—VALERIE HARBOUR.

Printed in the United States of America

PHOTO CREDITS

Bruce Coleman Ltd.—Jane Burton—10, 16, 80, 96, 99; J. Dermid—71; J. Simon—95; Bryce Canyon National Park—Utah—
85, 137; C.C.M. General Biological, Inc.—60, 81, 82, 83, 93, 119; Harris E. Duff—63, 81; Harry Engels—83; E.P.S.—69, 89, 112,
116; Hobby Fauna—136; Frankfurt Zoo—107; Lucio Gaggero—18, 64, 65, 75, 100, 101, 102, 103; Roy A. Harris and K. R. Duff—
119; Institute for Scientific Research—55; Frank Lane—56, 91, 108; Longo—137; Marineland of the Pacific, Los Angeles—133;
A. Margiocco—11, 22, 48, 49, 52, 53, 66, 75, 76, 77, 92, 95, 97, 98, 102, 104, 134, 136; J. Markham—London—42, 109; G. Mazza—
78; Meston Specialties—38, 39, 41, 43, 46, 75, 93, 108, 114; Museum of Natural History—G. Doria—16; Museum of Natural
History—Perugia—32, 33; Natural History Photo Agency—S. Dalton—12, 26, 94; J. Blossom—74; Charlie Off—60, 69; L. Oldrini—
Milan—93; Pasotti—66; Dr. Palnic—Venice—8; Dr. L. Pellegrini—Milan—85; Willis Peterson—45, 87, 133; Paul Popper—
London—10, 13, 84, 85, 119, 127, 128; Photo Researchers—118; Roebild—Muller—57, 81, 110; Roloc Color Slides—Washington—
56; Rome Zoo—36; A. P. Rossi—62, 65, 67, 114, 115, 116; Sirman—Dimt—40; Schmidt—136; Thonnard—Torno (Como)—79, 84;
Tiebilder—Okapia—6, 36, 37, 41, 142; Tomsick—68, 69, 70, 88; V-Dia Verlag—Heidelberg—95; Peter Ward—125; Jim Yoakum—71.

CONTENTS

The Chiroptera— Mammals on the Wing

Less knowledge and more superstition, prejudice, and apprehension exist about bats than about any other order of mammals. This stems largely from the single distinguishing feature of the order: the bat is the only mammal capable of true, sustained flight. Other so-called flying mammals simply glide.

It is difficult for the scientist to study an animal which spends its days sleeping and its nights flitting through the dark, and which responds badly to captivity. But it was easy for people in more superstitious times to invent all kinds of stories about an ugly, crinkly animal that flew through the night—along with ghosts and evil spirits. There were vampires (from the Serbian *wampir*), bloodsucking ghosts, dead men's souls which left their corpses at night to take blood from sleeping victims. The term was later applied to bloodsucking bats observed attacking animals in the tropics of the New World. When this news spread to Europe the existing fears of people were of course increased.

These negative feelings were not shared by all peoples, however. The Romans thought bats were sacred to the god of sleep, and some Caribbean peoples consider bats to be guardian angels of the home. In parts of Asia the flesh of the large fruit bats, cooked with herbs and spices, is considered a delicacy.

In fact, bats have both good and bad effects on man. On the bad side are the fruit bats, which can devastate an orchard, and the vampires, whose bite may cause infection and disease, such as rabies. But the other species, vastly more numerous, are a benefit to man, for they hold down insects harmful to him and his crops, pollinate fruit trees and, thanks to their gregarious cave-dwelling habits, they produce large quantities of guano, an excellent fertilizer.

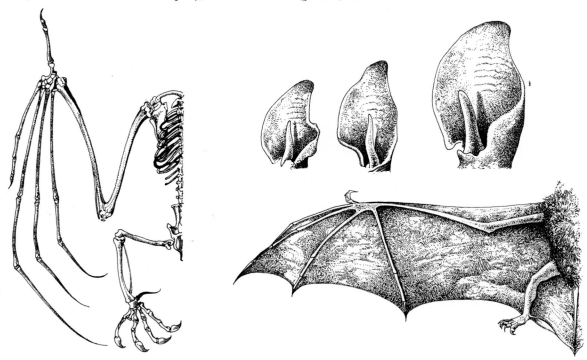

The three traguses (left) are examples of the appendages or lobes which are attached at the front of the bat's ear opening. They vary in size and enhance the hearing ability of the bat.

The bat's wing is made up of thin, light bones well adapted to flying. Finger and arm bones form the main wing structure.

Gould's fruit bat (Pteropus gouldii, opposite page) sometimes called a flying fox, eats the fruit of trees, then rests at the feeding site for several hours while digesting its meal.

(4) **carnivorous bats,** moderate in size, prey mostly on other small mammals, birds, lizards and frogs; (5) **vampires,** which make a shallow cut in the skin of a sleeping animal and lick up the oozing blood, are represented by three small species living only in Central and South America; (6) **fish-eating bats** hook up small fish swimming near the surface of the water with their powerful hind claws.

The order Chiroptera, which includes all the bats, is subdivided into two suborders—Megachiroptera (fruit- and nectar-eaters) and Microchiroptera (all others). Between them, they occupy all tropical and temperate parts of the world, except for a few remote islands. Of all mammals, only rodents exceed bats in number of species. Megachiroptera has one family, Pteropodidae. Microchiroptera is divided into 16 families and about 140 genera. In all there are more than 250 species of bats.

Pteropus, a fruit bat of Australia (right), hangs upside down squeezing the juice from a bunch of grapes. These bats will occasionally swallow some of the pulp if it is soft.

The dog-faced bat Rousettus (below) feeds mostly on fruit juices and flower nectar. These bats have been called "pollinators" because they transfer the pollen from flower to flower while seeking the nectar.

The flesh of flying foxes or fruit bats (Pteropus, left) is eaten by many natives and the fat is considered useful in treating rheumatism and baldness. This species is found on the islands in the Indian Ocean, the Philippines, the Marianas, Fiji, Samoa, eastern Australia, southeast Asia and Indonesia.

The Megachiroptera

Bats of this suborder are all fruit-eaters and are generally large, if not actually gigantic, when compared to the other suborder of insectivorous bats. They have a typical tooth form, with a wide and low crown and flat cuspids suitable for crushing fruit. The wingspan exceeds 3 feet in the larger species. The face has no fur around the nose which, with a few exceptions, has none of the appendages characeristic of many Microchiroptera.

The suborder consists of a single family, Pteropodidae, with 39 genera and some 130 species, variously distributed in all the hot, damp regions of the world, particularly southern Asia, the large island chains of the Pacific and Indian oceans, and Australia. Pteropodidae have a short tail or none at all. Almost all have a strong nail on the second finger. They have good eyes and navigate mostly by sight; only one genus, *Rousettus*, is known to emit ultrasonic cries while flying.

Briefly summarized, the principal genera of the Pteropodidae are the following:

Rousettus (13 species). These are the Rousette fruit bats, or "dog bats."

Pteropus (51 species). These are the fruit bats, or "flying foxes," with the largest wingspan of any bat species, up to 5 feet.

The epauleted bat Epomops (right), found only in Africa, has a wingspan of over 20 inches. This bat uses its expandible lips to fasten onto the fruit, while it pierces the rind with its canine teeth and squeezes out the juice with its jaws and tongue.

African fruit bats (opposite page) spend their days hanging in clusters from trees.

Dobsonia (9 species). These are the naked-backed fruit bats, characterized by the attachment of the naked wing membrane to the midline of the back, rather than to the flanks, as in all other bats.

Epomorphus (7 species). These so-called epauletted fruit bats have an 18-inch wingspan and a unique way of eating figs: they attach their bellowslike lips to the bottom and suck the fruit dry.

Macroglossus (4 species). These, the long-tongued fruit bats, use their tongues as a kind of drill to pierce the skin of very ripe fruit and draw out the pulp. They also eat nectar, and in the process pollinate flowers and are thus valued by fruit farmers.

The Microchiroptera

Most of the families of this order are insectivorous. In line with their feeding habits the fundamental characteristic is the shape of the molar crown which, unlike that of the Megachiroptera, is high, with sharp cusps. Another distinguishing feature is the lack of a claw on the second finger, this claw being especially useful to fruit bats, for it allows them to hang while feeding. Microchiroptera, as their name implies, are also usually smaller than the fruit bats.

This suborder consists of fully 16 families, with 141 genera and some 2,000 species distributed throughout the tropical and temperate world. Many species migrate south in the fall, while others go into a period of hibernation for as long as several months. Being insectivorous they play a fundamental role in the biological equilibrium of insects. The vampires or bloodsuckers are also among the Microchiroptera. Following

The brown bat (Myotis) is the most widely distributed of all the bats, being found throughout the world except in the Arctic and Antarctic regions and many oceanic islands. Its flight is mostly slow and straight. Brown bats roost during the days in caves, attics, towers and sometimes trees and tall jungle grasses. There are about 60 species. Their diet consists of insects caught on the wing. While feeding, they frequently stop and hang for a while to digest the catch, and then again take to flight for more food.

is a list of the 16 families, included in this order, along with descriptions of their major characteristics.

Rhinopomatidae—
The Mouse-tailed Bats

Ths family includes only one genus, *Rhinopoma*. The common name derives from their long and slender tails, which extend far beyond the tail membrane. Their range includes Sumatra, Thailand and climatically compatible areas of western Asia and northeast Africa. A typical species is *R. microphyllum*. Bats of this species are 2½ to 3 inches long, with tails slightly longer than the head and body length. The snout is chunky, short and flattened, with a small nose leaf; ears are large and pointed, connected by a skin bridge and equipped with a tragus—a small projection at the front of the ear opening which helps focus the received sound waves. They have a very long forearm. Rhinopomatids feed on water insects and in the course of a night destroy a great many of those that fly over lagoons and ponds in river deltas, while by day they cluster in caves and ruins. (In North Africa they congregate in certain pyramids during daylight.)

Emballonuridae—
The Sheath-tailed Bats

There are twelve genera in this family, distributed in all tropical and subtropical regions of the world. All of medium size, these bats are easily identified by the short tail which pierces the tail membrane near the base and protrudes above. Also characteristic are their large, widespread ears and their pointy, unadorned noses. Of the twelve genera, *Taphozus*, and particularly the species *T. perforatus*, is distinguished from the other emballonurids by a deep furrow across the forehead. The head and body measure

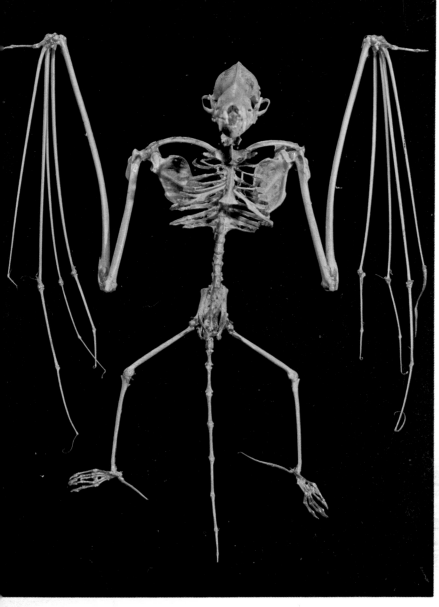

about 2½ inches long and the tail 1 inch; the face is triangular. Brownish-gray fur covers the upper body and throat, while the breast and abdomen are grayish. These bats have typically insectivorous feeding habits. *Taphozus* lives in northeast Africa and parts of western Arabia. In Egypt, where the ancient tombs are a favorite daytime resting place for these bats, they are sometimes called "tomb bats."

Noctilionidae— Bulldog and Fisherman Bats

This family comprises a single genus, *Noctilio*, with two species found in the American tropics and subtropics. They are very similar except for the hind legs. *N. leporinus* has long legs and large feet used for catching fish, while *N. labialis*, being insectivorous, has more conventional legs and feet. Both have very narrow wings with the membrane ending at the hip, which frees the legs from the wing action. The large tail membrane, however, covers the whole rear edge of the limb. The head is large and roundish, and the pointed ears are attached at the sides. The fishing bat is about 4 inches long. The male has long orange-rufous back fur which

A bat skeleton (above) shows the powerful shoulder girdle and weak pelvis and legs.

The molar of the pipistrelle bat, similar to that of an insectivore, is well adapted for crushing insects.

The tomb bat Taphozous (far right), has a pocket or pouch in the membrane of its wing near the shoulder. There it can store its food of flying insects.

becomes whitish toward the front; the membrane is dark brown. The feet are wide and strong with long toes equipped with strong curved nails. The bat's flight is linear, without sudden turns. *N. leporinus* fishes by dragging a foot in the water and hooking up small surface-swimming fish, which it immediately puts in its mouth. It may swallow the fish in flight or tuck it into a cheek pouch to be devoured at greater leisure while roosting nearby.

Nycteridae— Slit-faced Bats

These bats acquire their name from a characteristic slit, partially obscured by nose leaves, that runs up the whole face from the nostrils up to the forehead. They have large wings and a well developed tail that extends to the end of the membrane and there forms a T-shaped tip which offers support to the trailing edge. This is a unique structure among mammals. They feed on insects, emitting ultrasonic squeaks as they fly. They also have a voice audible to humans, which sounds like a "tic" or "clink." The ears are very large, with a small, chunky tragus. The fur is soft and grayish-brown all over. The wingspan sometimes exceeds

12 inches. This family consists of a single genus, *Nycteris*, with about ten species found mostly in southern Africa below the Sahara, and sometimes in southern Asia, the most familiar being the Theban slit-faced bat.

Megadermatidae— False Vampire Bats

Unlike most bats, the species of this family are not insectivorous but feed on comparatively large prey such as rodents, birds, fish and bats of other families. The name "false vampire" reflects the old but wrong belief that they feed on blood, as do the true vampires of the New World. They may first drink the blood of their prey, but unlike vampires they also eat the flesh, like carnivores. They have long, erect nose leaves but lack upper incisor teeth and have no visible tails. Most startling, perhaps, are their ears, which are huge, upright and united at the base. They apparently fly with their mouths closed, emitting ultrasonic sounds through their noses. Of the three genera and five species, *Lavia frons* is not known to be carnivorous, but feeds mainly on insects. It clings to a branch and, when it detects an insect, swoops down like a flycatcher in pursuit. Later it returns to its perch. The most familiar spe-

Pipistrellus, the pipistrelle bat (below and left), is the first bat to appear in the evening and has even been spotted in broad daylight. It has characteristic long, sharp incisors and small, rounded tongue.

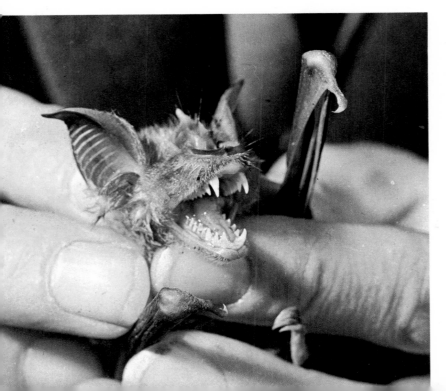

cies is the Australian false vampire (*Macroderma gigas*), found in the band of tropical forests of northern Australia. Its membranes are pinkish-brown, and the fur is gray on the back and white on the breast and belly. A carnivore which preys on other bats and small mammals, it hunts in packs; now and then one member leaves the group to attack its prey, which it rapidly devours, then returns to the others.

Rhinolophidae—Horseshoe Bats

This family includes two genera of insectivorous bats, one of which (*Rhinolophus*) contains about 50 species found in Europe and as far east as Australia and Japan. The other genus (*Rhinomagalophus*) has one species, the only example of which was found in Indochina. It features a peculiar three-part nose leaf comprised of a horseshoe-shaped lower section which covers the upper lip and surrounds the nostrils, a central projecting divider and an erect, complex, pointed structure so large as partly to obscure the small eyes. Flying with their mouths closed, horseshoe bats emit ultrasonic sounds through their nostrils. The large, pointed ears lack a tragus. The female has two functioning mammary glands on her chest, and two teatlike formations on the abdomen which probably serve as graspers for an infant carried in flight. Wings are broad, tail membranes are short, and the flight character of these bats is fluttering and hovering. People throughout Europe believed that horseshoe bats not only were insect-eaters but were also vampires, preferring the blood of farm animals. They do indeed approach animals in their stalls, but only to catch the insects that congregate there. The fur of the various species ranges from reddish-brown to deep black above and paler below. When sleeping, Rhinolophidae wrap themselves completely in their wings and tail membranes, looking like fruit pods or large cocoons. While hibernating in this position their body temperature has been known to drop to 46° F.

The greater horseshoe bat Rhinolophus ferrumequinum *(right and far right) lives in caves, hollow trees and buildings. In cold regions these bats hibernate during the winter.*

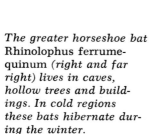

Hipposideridae—
Old World Leaf-nosed Bats

This family includes nine genera and about 40 species. In general these bats resemble the Rhinolophidae, but the nose leaf lacks the central projecting divider, the toes have only two bones each instead of the usual three, the structure of the shoulder and hip girdles differs substantially, and the lower small premolars are missing. Even so, some writers treat this family as a suborder of

Feeding on spiders and flying insects, the greater horseshoe bat goes out to search for its meals late in the evening and often returns to its roost to eat.

The green areas of the map show the range of members of the genus Rhinolophus, the horseshoe bats.

The faces of the different species of the American leaf-nosed bats (Phyllostomidae) are varied. The drawings illustrate the bizarre shapes and sizes of the traguses and nose leaves.

Rhinolophidae. A typical species of Hipposideridae is the trident leaf-nosed bat (*Asellia tridens*), which is rather small (about 2¼ inches long, plus a 1-inch tail). The upper structure of the nose leaf divides into three pointed leaflets, whence the common name. In males there is a small sac behind this appendage containing a waxy substance which can be ejected at will, particularly during the mating season. The ears are medium-sized and pointed-oval; the fur is fine with a wide variety of shadings, usually

ical species distributed primarily in South America and the Antilles, with a few species in North America. Their size varies from species to species, ranging from mouse-size to not much smaller than most Megachiroptera. The wings are large in relation to the body. The dentition consists of a maximum of 34 teeth almost exclusively typical of insect eaters. The ears are attached low on the sides of the head, though their shape and size vary from species to species; the face always has large and occasionally complex

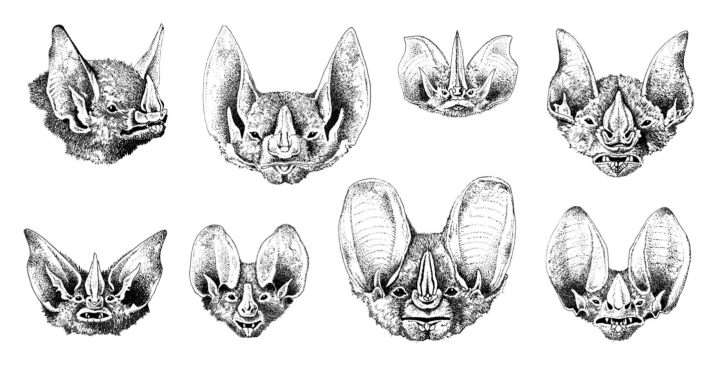

brown on the upper and whitish on the lower parts of the body. *A. tridens* ranges across North Africa to Egypt, southward to Zanzibar and eastward to northern India.

Phyllostomatidae—
New World Leaf-nosed Bats

This family of 51 genera and approximately 140 species, one of the largest of the Microchiroptera, includes a large number of trop-

nose leaves. Phyllostomids were believed for many generations to be insatiable bloodsuckers and were therefore subjected to unremitting persecution, but it has now been fully demonstrated that they feed almost exclusively on insects, which they destroy in enormous numbers. A few species are carnivorous, and some feed on fruit and the nectar of flowers, to the advantage of agriculture. Brief descriptions of the most familiar species follow.

The Spear-nosed Bat (*Phyllostomus hastatus*) is the second largest member of the family. The head and ears are small, but its body is chunky and robust and its wingspan attains 19 inches. The nose leaf rises flat, broad and pointed at the top like a spear-head from an almost piglike snout. The fur, very fine and long, is uniformly russet. The various species of the genus are all restricted to the hot and damp tropical regions of Central America and northern South America, where they are called "vampires" by the local

that in its nocturnal flights through the shady forests of southern Mexico, Peru and Brazil, it feeds partly on fruit and insects but mostly on birds, small rodents and other bats. It is reddish-brown above and slightly paler below. Its face is flanked by large, oval ears and comes to a point, with a large, spearlike nose leaf.

The Wrinkle-faced Bat (*Centurio senex*) resembles the other Central American fruit bats in most regards, but is distinguished

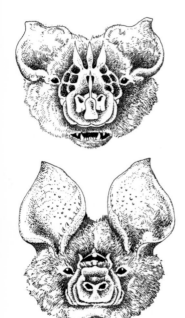
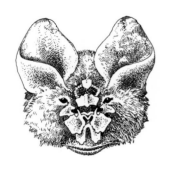

The skull of the leaf-nosed bat (left) shows the dental formula characteristic of the Phillostomidae family.

people. They are not blood-drinkers, but they are carnivorous, feeding on mice, small bats, birds and insects. In captivity, they also eat such fruit as figs and bananas.

The False Vampire (*Vampyrus spectrum*) is the largest of the Phyllostomatids, with a wingspan of 20 inches and a slightly larger and heavier body than the spear-nosed bat. It was for a long time believed to be a true vampire bat, but it has now been established

externally by two remarkable features. Its wings bear a light and dark lattice-like pattern between the third and fourth fingers and its face is unique in the bat world. The head is round with a high brain case and a very short nose. The face is naked and entirely covered with grotesque wrinkles and lappets of skin. A large chin flap drops down when the bat hangs at rest, completely enveloping the face and ears, which fold downward. The portion of skin which covers the eyes is trans-

The mouse-eared bat Myotis myotis (below) has an erect and tapering tragus. Its brilliant coloring, small eyes and sharp teeth are characteristic of its species.

The colored areas of the top map indicate the habitat of the Desmodontidae, or vampire bats, in the tropical areas of Central and South America.

The almost worldwide distribution of Vespertilionidae is indicated in red on the bottom map.

lucent, allowing the bat to tell day from night through the hood. It roosts in trees, usually in twos and threes.

The Fly-catching Bat (*Glossophaga soricina*) is one of the three species whose range extends from northern Mexico and the Bahama Islands south to Argentina. It feeds throughout the night on insects, fruit and flower nectar. The snout is long, the tongue is extensible and covered with bristlelike papillae. Its diet includes the petals of flowers, which it tears off by means of its long tongue. It is rather small, and its wingspan rarely reaches 10 inches. The body is covered by a very thick coat, colored in various shades from brown to reddish-brown.

The Striped Vampire (*Vampyrops helleri*) is quite small, with no visible tail; its name

comes from two handsome white stripes running along the sides of its face and a single stripe running along its spine. The fur on its back is dark brown or black and extends outward to its elbows. The ears are medium-sized the nose leaf is tall and pointed. *Vampyrops'* range extends from

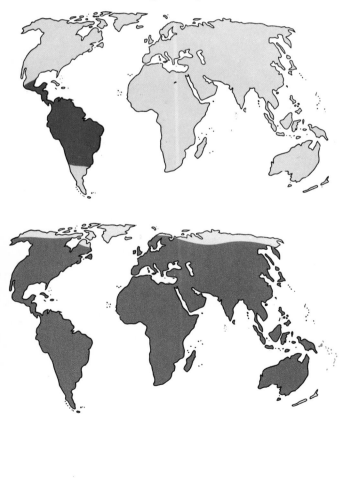

southern Mexico south to Peru and east to Trinidad. Fruit makes up the major portion of its diet, along with some insects.

The Yellow-shouldered or **Fleur-de-lis Vampire** (*Sturnira lillium*) has an erect nose leaf flanked by two smaller leaflets, which ap-

pear somewhat like the stylized lily of French heraldry. It is distinguished by tufts of stiff, yellowish hair at the shoulder. Its teeth, like those of fruit bats, are modified to perforate the tough skin of certain fruits. It is quite small, only 2½ inches long. There is no tail, and the tail membrane is very narrow and fringed with fur. The legs and feet are furred to the claws. It is a rather common forest bat, found from Mexico to Argentina. There are four species.

The Neotropical Fruit Bat (*Artibeus jamaicensis*), like a few other Phyllostomatids, is

tailless, and the tail membrane is very small. The fur is soft, velvety and short; the upper parts are gray, brownish or black. Members of this genus vary greatly in size and weight, the smallest being about 2 inches long and weighing under half an ounce. The largest, *A. literatus*, stretches 4 inches and weighs almost 3 ounces. Their habitat is quite varied, and their range extends from northern New Mexico south to Argentina and eastward through Brazil and the West Indies. They eat such fruit as figs, mangoes, avocados, bananas and some nuts.

Desmodontidae— Vampire Bats

The story of these bats is fraught with leg-

end and error. The eminent French naturalist Buffon, in his famous *Natural History* published in 1749, quoted the testimony of naturalists and travelers as well as his own experience and named these bats "vampires," thus implying that they suck the blood of humans. In fact, vampires only rarely attack man. They do attack other large animals, however, such as horses and cattle, by selecting a sparsely haired spot and making a small, superficial bite in the skin with their incisors. Then they gorge themselves on the oozing blood by sucking it through the tubelike space formed between the tongue and

A little brown bat (Myotis bechsteini) shows its echo-location system in flight—The mouth is partially open, directing high frequency cries; the ears are erect and facing forward to receive the echos. All four limbs and the tail hold the flying membrane taut, ready to respond instantly to the signals received.

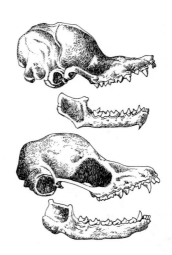

The skull of the smokey bat Furipteridae (above, top) shows the high forehead and small canine teeth typical of this family. The skull of the sucker-footed bat (Thyropteridae) has a long, slender snout and elongated canines.

The feeding flight of the noctule bat (Nyctalus noctuls) begins around sunset and may last up to two hours. A second feeding flight takes place just before sunrise. These bats fly fast and execute quick, sharp turns. The mouth is kept open continually allowing them to capture and swallow the insects they encounter en route.

the notched lower lip. The wound is small but heals slowly. The real danger lies in the possibility that rabies may be transmitted and that the open wounds may become infected or offer entry to parasitic worms.

Vampires, which range from northern Mexico to Argentina, are so common in some areas as to make stock-raising unprofitable. They sleep during the day in caves and other places of total darkness, emerging at dusk to feed. A vampire flies low and straight; after selecting an animal, it often lands nearby and walks across the ground and up its leg. Vampires seldom attack dogs, probably because a dog can hear high-frequency

sounds and thus be warned by the bat's cries as it approaches. Desmodontids have 20 to 26 teeth, with a single pair of large, sharp incisors. They are of medium size, with a wingspan not exceeding 12 inches. Three genera of one species each make up the family.

The Common Vampire (*Desmodus rotundus*) is innocuous in appearance and is easily mistaken for a more ordinary bat, even by the people of Central America and those South American countries where it lives (Chile, Argentina, Bolivia, Colombia, Venezuela, Brazil, Paraguay and Uruguay). This rather

The Hairy-legged Vampire (*Diphylla ecaudata*) is distinguished from the two preceding desmodontids by the smaller size of its body, by the small ears and by the number of teeth (26). It is found only in tropical America, as far north as southern Mexico.

Furipteridae—
The Smoky Bats

The natives of South America call these bats by a name which means "winged fury," descriptive of their lightning speed of attack as they hunt insects. These are small bats whose heads and bodies are slightly over 2 inches long, but whose wings may attain a span of 10 inches. They have a small face, with a short nose ending in a small disk. The ears are large and pointed and set so low that the bases cover the eyes. The thumb is not visible, though a short, functionless claw can be seen. They live in the South American tropics. The two known genera have a single species each—*Amorphochilus schnablii,* which is found in western Ecuador, western Peru and northern Chile, and *Furipterus horrens,* found in Panama, Colombia and Brazil.

Thyropteridae—
The Disk-winged Bats

The single genus Thyroptera is represented by two species which are among the most bizarre of mammals. *T. tricolor* is small, with a short, hairy face and no nose leaf. It is brownish-red on top, white on the belly and black on the back of the ears. The tail extends slightly beyond a large tail membrane. The third and fourth toes are joined. But the most remarkable feature is its device for roosting. Instead of hanging from a crevice by the toe claws, as most bats do, this bat hangs head-up by means of four suction disks mounted in short stalks and lo-

sedentary animal hunts usually at night. It has dark, grayish-brown fur, a small head, pointed ears, a flat, snoutlike nose and only 20 teeth. Its retreats usually have a strong odor of ammonia emanating from the pools of digested blood present in their droppings.

The White-winged Vampire (*Diaemus youngi*) behaves like the preceding species but is restricted to the Amazon forest. It is unique among bats in that it has 22 teeth. *Diaemus* prefers the blood of birds and goats. Its color is cinnamon brown with a touch of red overall except for the borders and tips of the wings, which are white.

The comparison of the two skulls (below) of the Vespertilionidae family, genus Myotis *(top) and* Pipistrellus *(bottom) reveals that the latter has fewer teeth.*

The flight of the pipistrelle bats (right, top center and below) is jerky and erratic. Their roosting sites include hollow trees, buildings, caves and rocky crevices.

The little brown bat Myotis *(opposite page, far right top) flys slow and straight. It alternates its feeding flights with rest periods during which time it digests its meals.*

A baby bat clings to its mother in flight. It remains attached to her breast, supported by her wings, when she roosts upside down. (opposite page, below)

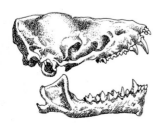

cated on the hands at the base of the thumb and on the soles of each foot. They roost inside fronds or rolled leaves, usually from the banana tree (*Heliconia*). *T. discifera* resembles *T. tricolor* except that it has a brownish belly and larger yellowish ears. Both species eat insects, usually hunting among the wide-leafed trees. They are found in the tropical area of northern South America.

Vespertilionidae— Common Bats

This family includes the most common European bats of the area ranging from the plains to the mountains, from the Mediterranean to the North Sea. They are small and have none of the excrescences or nose leaves that characterize most other bats. This fam-

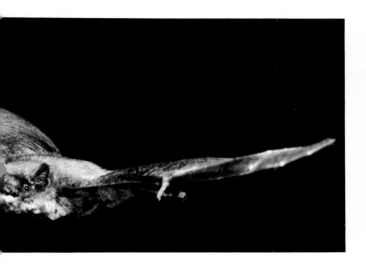

ily of 38 genera and about 275 species is represented in every part of the world but is most abundant in Europe. The most familiar genera are *Myotis, Pipistrellus, Eptesicus, Nyctalus, Vespertilio, Barbastella, Miniopterus,* and *Plecotus*.

Pipistrelles (*Pipistrellus kuhli*) are the commonest of the bats living in Europe, and they are also found in North America, Asia and North Africa. They are smaller than *Myotis,* which they generally resemble except for the coloring of the ventral region, somewhat darker in *P. kuhli*.

The Big Brown Bat (*Eptesicus fuscus*) is large in comparison to most other insectivorous bats, with a wingspan of 13 inches. The genus Eptesicus contains 30 species with practically worldwide distribution, favoring the plains for the rivers and stagnant water to be found there. They skim the surface, hunting a variety of insects, including water beetles.

The Little Brown Bat (*Myotis myotis*) is common throughout Europe. Its head and body together measure about 3 inches, its tail 2½ inches, and its wingspan 15 inches. The coat, varying from gray to brown on the back,

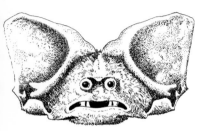

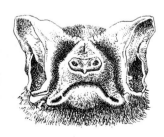

is whitish on the abdomen. Found also in North Africa and Asia, it is adapted to a wide range of climates and surroundings, including large cities, where it takes advantage of the street lamps that attract the insects on which it feeds.

The Noctule Bat (*Nyctalus noctula*) holds the record for size among European bats, with its 15-inch wingspan, 3-inch body and 2-inch tail. It is characterized by a garliclike odor emanating from its axillary glands and by its rapid flight, punctuated by sharp turns and bursts of piercing, staccato cries as it pursues insect prey at dusk and dawn. *N. noctula* has a face like that of a miniature wombat, with larger ears.

The Barbastelle (*Barbastella barbastellus*) has broad, notched ears, covered by soft fur on the back side and united by a low membrane. The face is very short, and the eye is actually surrounded by the broad-based ear structure. Its range extends from England

through Germany and Scandinavia to Russia. The only other species, *B. leucolemas*, ranges from the Caucasus through Turkestan and southern Asia. They hibernate from September to April, except for occasional winter flights.

The Frosted Bat (*Vespertilio murinus*) prefers the cool damp climate of northern and central Europe. It appears in late evening and usually flies higher than 50 feet above the ground. Its coat is blackish-brown above with white-tipped hairs that give it a "frosted" look. The ears are short and broad, and the face has a short upturned snout.

The Swallow Bat or Bent-winged Bat (*Miniopterus schreibersi*) owes its name to the long wings which, when the bat is hanging by its feet, fold back on themselves at the first finger joint. The tail, longer than the body, is enclosed by a long membrane. It roosts in caves, culverts, eaves and trees. Swallow bats sometimes appear in swarms, early in the evening, in rapid, jerky flight. The ten species range through Africa, southern Europe and across southern Asia.

The Big-eared Bat or Lump-nosed Bat (*Plecotus auritus*) has huge, saillike ears. The tragus itself is as big as the ears of some bats. When the bat is at rest the ears coil alongside the head or tuck under the wings. Their flight, which starts after dark, is slow, with frequent hovering stops, like the flight of a butterfly. Some of the five species have large fleshy nodules between the eyes. *P. auritus* lives in Eurasia, the others range from southern Canada to Mexico.

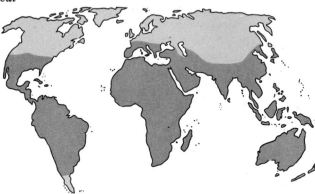

Molossidae— Free-tailed Bats

The common names refer respectively to the ratlike tail, which extends far beyond the membrane, and to the head and snout, which

The ears of the barbastelle bat have characteristically notched edges.

resemble those of molossid, or mastiff-type dogs. This family of about 12 genera and 80 species inhabits most of the temperate land masses. The head and body length varies from 1½ to 5 inches. The short body hair is velvety; the ears are thick and leathery. There is no nose leaf, and the lips are large. Wings are long, narrow and leathery; the foot is broad, with the hind toe of each equipped with spoon-shaped bristles used for grooming. The teeth are normal for insect eaters.

Free-tailed Bats (*Tadarida*) include about 35 species, native to most of the warm areas of the world. Some bat species roost in small groups, others in groups of hundreds or thousands, but *T. brasiliensis* congregates literally by the millions in some large caves in the United States. Among the great sights of the animal world are the sky-darkening swarms of bats that emerge early each evening from the Carlsbad Caverns in New Mexico, to the accompaniment of the soft, fluttering roar of their wings and the chittering chorus of their cries. So many millions of bats roosted there for so many thousands of years that their droppings eventually attracted commercial fertilizer interests. For 15 years, six months a year, guano was mined from the floor of the cave and hauled away at the rate of 50 to 100 tons per day. It is hard to believe that all this guano was made up of the carcasses of insects that had passed through the stomachs of 2-ounce bats. Carlsbad is a big cave, but it is only one roost out of thousands used by this species, which is only one of several hundred bat species. Pondering this should give some idea of the bat's role in the ecology as a controller of insects.

The big-eared bats Macrotus (above and left) fly in a slow, uncertain pattern reminiscent of a butterfly. The nose-leaf is erect and shaped like an arrowhead.

The slow, flapping flight of the barbastelle bat (below) takes place before sunset. They often fly close to the ground seeking food.

Dermoptera—the "flying lemurs"

This order includes only two very similar species, sometimes called flying lemurs. They are not actually lemurs, though the head resembles a lemur's head, and they share the same staring expression of the eyes. Nor do they actually fly, in the sense that a bat or a bird flies—they only glide, but they glide remarkably well. *Cynocephalus volans* lives in the southern Philippines, and *C. variegatus* inhabits southern Indochina, Sumatra, Java and Borneo. Of the size of a small cat, they seek the forested areas, where they rest and sleep by day high in the tall trees, either nestling in a hollow or hanging from a branch by the powerful claws on all four feet.

At dusk they launch into the air and glide to the food trees. Flights of 100 yards are not unusual, with an altitude loss of only 40 or 50 feet. Some observers report even greater flight efficiency. A colugo (a native name) with good control may alight on the trunk of a tree; another may land on the ground and struggle clumsily to the base of a tree. The gliding membrane is quite large, extending from the neck to the knuckles of the front feet, straight back to the toes of the rear feet, and from there to the tip of the long tail. It is muscled, and

when the animal climbs, slowly but skillfully, the membrane is tucked under the forelegs to keep it out of the way. After a night of feeding on fruits, buds, flowers and leaves the colugo returns to the nest tree. Its voice is a rasping cry which probably serves as an alarm signal.

The coat is silky, the color generally mottled brown in the male and grayer in the female. Scattered white spots on the back fur help *C. variegatus* to blend with the tree bark. The lower incisors are formed like miniature combs, with as many as 12 "comb teeth" per tooth. These teeth superficially resemble the comb teeth of the lemurs but are structurally quite different and are used for both food-straining and grooming. A single young is born after a gestation period of about 60 days. Until weaned the baby may be left in the tree or may fly with the mother, clinging to her belly fur and nursing from one of two nipples near her armpits.

Classification of colugos has been difficult. Some naturalists put them with the lemurs or the insectivores, in spite of their obvious differences. The fossil record is unclear. The fossils in Asia go back only 10,000 years. In America an extinct family, Plagiomenidae, dating from the Paleocene period 60,000,000 years ago, may be related to the present dermoptera. In any event continuity is lacking. Finally some authorities established a separate order, but the controversy still exists.

The skeleton shows the thin, light limbs of Cynocephalus, *the flying or gliding lemurs.*

The colored areas of the map represent the range of the Dermoptera. The flying lemur (opposite page) has a large gliding membrane which is attached to the neck, limbs and tail, allowing it to glide up to 400 feet.

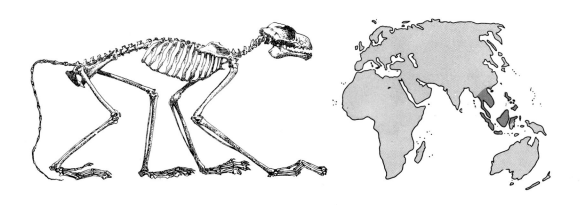

Edentata—The Toothless Ones

Every animal has a dental arrangement to suit its need. As the need varies, so do the teeth. A carnivore has some teeth designed as weapons that stab and tear, others that function as slicers and crushers of meat and bone. An ungulate's teeth are flat and broad for mashing grass to a pulp. Rodents have some teeth that cut like a chisel, and others designed to grind seeds. Occasionally, however, teeth are too few in number, too weak or are lacking entirely. Some whales, for example, live on tiny plankton which they strain out of the water and compress into masses with the tongue. They have no use for teeth and consequently have none.

The lack or drastic reduction of teeth appears in other groups too. The big American anteater has no teeth; it needs none for its peculiar diet. The pangolin, which also eats ants, has a similar mouth, and so does the African anteater, the aardvark, though it does have a few molars. Early zoologists, taking this similarity as a basis, grouped these three together into the single order, Edentata—the toothless ones. Today this grouping is no longer considered valid. Long ago the aardvark was removed from the classification because of a clear relationship with the ungulates. Its nails are constructed like hoofs, and many other parts are similar to the corresponding parts of ungulates. But it is not an ungulate either, so it was designated with an order of its own, Tubulidentata, after its tubular teeth.

It also became clear that the pangolins were different in many respects from the group which includes the American anteaters, the sloths and the armadillos. The similarity of the pangolin's mouth to that of the American anteater is now regarded as a similar adaptation to a common way of life rather than as an indication of related ancestry.

The drawings show, from above: The hooklike claws of the three-toed sloth, which are also used as weapons of defense. The paw of the giant anteater has a pad for walking and strong claws used for tearing apart anthills. The paw of the tamandua also has a pad for walking and three claws, one of which is huge. The skull of the tamandua shows a structure for the long, tubular snout, well suited to its diet of ants and termites. The sloth's skull shows the short muzzle and weak teeth. The skull of the armadillo also lacks canine and incisor teeth, and the molars are almost useless.

The giant anteater (opposite page) amazed early explorers, who had never seen anything like it. They called it an "ant bear" because of its coarse coat and huge size. This head-on picture shows the tremendous length of the snout and the way it holds its claws up when it walks.

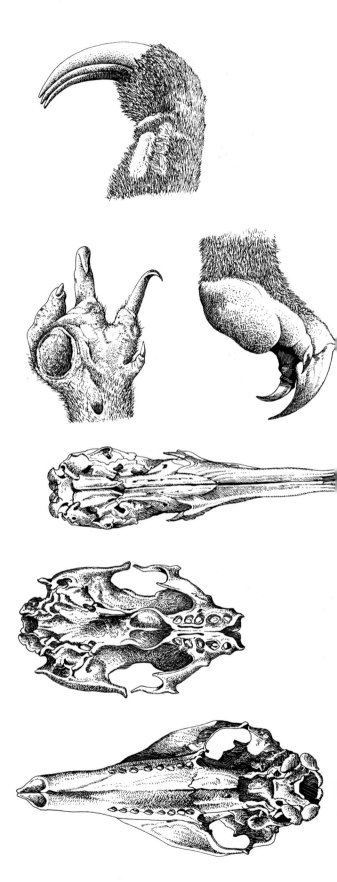

Important wrist bones of the pangolin are fused, whereas in the Edentata they are separate. Other important skeletal structures are clearly unique, so it is proper to separate pangolins from the Edentata and give them an order of their own: Pholidota—the scaly ones.

The ancestors of the edentates, which have come down to us in fossil form since the Eocene some 50 million years ago, did have teeth, however. On the basis of a study of successive geological strata, moreover, it is possible to reconstruct the chain of events that brought about the disappearance of a feature as apparently indispensable as teeth. We know of herbivorous Edentata that possessed the typical dentition of herbivores—the Gravigrada, or sloths. They were huge and thick-set, with prehensile forepaws. The gigantic armored Glyptodonts of the Pliocene and the Quaternary had teeth like a rodent's. The evolutionary process that has led in certain cases to the total disappearance of teeth probably followed the most obvious road.

The tamandua (right) spends most of its time in trees, where it seeks ants, termites and bees. It is active mostly at night and uses its strong tail as a climbing aid.

Forms with specialized dentitions evolved into forms with teeth that were all alike and that subsequently became fewer and then disappeared. This conclusion may be drawn from fossil remains and from studies of the few forms still in being today, but it is not easy to support this hypothesis with certainty. Indeed, to describe the evolution of any group is to attempt to describe a great buried tree, deducing its shape from the few branches that pierce the surface.

In general, the Edentata have almost

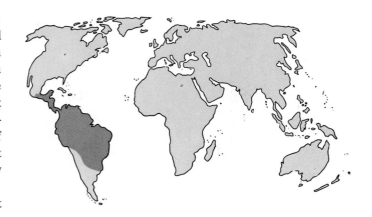

The colored areas of the map show the range of the giant anteater and the other South American anteaters.

Giant anteaters are mostly solitary animals. The only exceptions to their lonely habits occur during the mating season.

uniform, permanent teeth, which are not preceded by milk teeth and which have neither enamel nor roots. In some instances the body is covered by strong, horny plates; in others, there is a long, thick fur. All Edentata living today are plantigrade; occasionally a toe may be dwarfed or absent, but the rest are always equipped with talons. Living edentates are subdivided into three families, chiefly on the basis of the shape of the skull and the type of body covering. The family of the Myrmecophagidae includes the giant anteater (*Myrmecophaga tridactyla*), the long-tailed lesser anteater (*Tamandua tetradactyla*) and the common anteater (*Cyclopes didactylus*) The Bradypodidae include five species of sloths in the genus *Bradypus* and two in the genus *Choloepus*.

The little two-toed ant-eater moves with delicacy and grace among the slenderest of branches. The mouth opening is about the size of a lead pencil. To compensate for a lack of teeth, a portion of the stomach is built like a gizzard to grind up the ants it eats.

The skull of the two-toed anteater shows the tubular muzzle and the weak, toothless lower jaw.

A tamandua attacks an anthill (bottom). This individual was photographed in a zoo, where it lives in an artificially created environment.

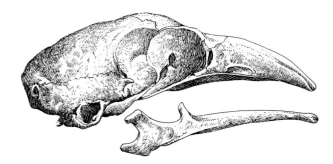

Myrmecophagidae— Anteaters and Tamanduas

The Giant Anteater (*Myrmecophaga tridactyla*) owes its name to its size, which is truly staggering: it can grow to be more than 7 feet long, thanks to its long tail, which alone measures more than 3 feet. This huge animal, which can weigh as much as 100 pounds, lives solely on ants and termites. Its entire organism seems to have been designed for this purpose. Its foot-long head ends in a long, pointed muzzle that turns down toward the ground. Its mouth conceals a weapon that is terrible against ants: a slender, cylindrical, viscous tongue, about 16 inches long. Its eyes are small; its ears are short and

the temperature of the air. It may go as low as 75° F. or as high as 90°. As a result, sloths can live only in an equatorial climate and must avoid the direct sun. Even mating is carried out with the incredible slowness that seems to rule this species. Pregnancy lasts four to six months. The baby sloth already has claws and remains firmly attached to its mother throughout the suckling period.

The other sloths show only a few minor differences from the three-toed species. The two-toed, which belongs to the genus *Choloepus*, has a large head, a squat muzzle and a flat forehead. The legs look thin; the hands have two claws while the feet have three. The dentition consists of sharp upper and lower canines, and 8 blunt grinding teeth in the back of the upper jaw and 6 in the lower. *Choloepus didactylus*, which lives in the forests of Guiana and Surinam, is about 27 inches long and has a grayish-olive color. The muzzle and the sole of the feet are pink. The other species of the genus (*C. hoffmani*) differs in some skeletal characteristics and lacks the third digit on the forepaw. The two-toed sloths are the most "dynamic" of the Bradypodidae, moving less slowly and reacting vigorously with their claws in self-defense in the event of attack.

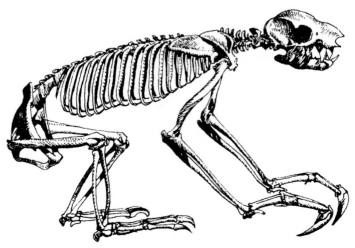

A three-toed sloth goes out on a slender limb. The mottled appearance of its coat results from variations in the density of the algae that grow in its hair.

The skeleton of a two-toed sloth shows the elongated limbs and the pelvis adapted for upside-down suspension. The rib cage is long to cradle the internal organs. The sharp incisor teeth are sometimes used for defense.

Dasypodidae— The Armadillo Family

This family is one of the most exceptional in the animal kingdom, though today only a few species remain from the group that appeared in the Cenozoic with the Glyptodonts. Those gigantic armored animals were covered with strong, rigidly united, bony plates. Even the armadillos observed today retain this interesting feature, but they are paltry descendants of a great race, since they are rarely more than 16 inches long. A prehistoric monster still lives among us, but in miniature.

Besides the horny armor, the general characteristics of this group include a skull with long bones and a tubular muzzle terminating in a small mouth. The number of teeth varies from several dozen up to a whopping 90, all similar and without enamel or roots. The tongue is slender and the body is thick, in the shape of an elongated hemisphere with a conical tail. The stomach is short, and so is the intestine.

Armadillos can be subdivided roughly into five main groups. The first is represented by the hairy armadillo, the six-banded armadillo, and the pichi.

The Hairy Armadillo (*Chaetophractus villosis*) has a shell composed of a complicated system of plates and small scales. These develop from the deepest layer of the skin, the derma, which is ossified and covered by a horny layer. Small scales on the head are joined together to form a thick, highly protective armor. The back armor is composed of eight articulated transverse bands. Among the various plates on the back there are a few bristles of moderate length. The belly lacks armor protection but is covered with long whitish hair. When this armadillo is threatened, it draws in its legs until the edges of the carapace touch the ground. The hairy armadillo lives in Argentina and Uruguay.

The Six-banded Armadillo (*Euphractus sexcinctus*) is distinguished from the hairy armadillo by the division of its dorsal armor into six rather than eight bands. When alarmed, at first it attempts to run away. If caught, it lowers the carapace to the ground. It will fight with teeth and claws if knocked over. The head is protected by a sturdy upper shell that runs back as far as the ears. The six-banded armadillo is a nocturnal animal which lives in Brazil, Bolivia and Paraguay, by preference on level ground.

The nine-banded armadillo (opposite page) can roll almost into a ball when it is frightened. It is active mostly at night, busily poking into holes and crevices as it seeks insects or an occasional snake or lizard to eat.

The map shows the range of the Dasypodidae family, the armadillos and pichichiegos.

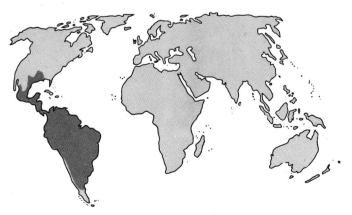

The Pichi (*Zaedyus pichiy*) is distinguished by its sharp muzzle and short ears.

The second group includes the giant armadillo and five species of the genus *Cabassous*, most typical of which is the **large-eared armadillo** (*Cabassous unicinctus*).

The Giant Armadillo (*Priodontes giganteus*) is the largest of the armadillos, measuring as much as 40 inches, not including the tail, and weighing up to 120 pounds. Its dorsal bands may vary from 11 to 13 inches. Its entire shell is black except on the head, the tail and the flanks, which are grayish. The claws are strong and long, that of the third finger measuring 7 inches along the curve. This animal is quite agile and frequently balances on the hind legs and tail. When alarmed, it tries to roll up, but the shell is not large enough to completely enclose it. It is found mostly in Brazil, usually near the water. It has many small, weak, peglike teeth —sometimes as many as 100. The giant armadillo feeds at night on ants, termites, worms, spiders, larvae, snakes and carrion, digging prodigiously for its food.

The Genus *Tolypeutes* includes two species of the **Three-banded Armadillo,** *T. matacus* and *T. tricinctus*. This is the only armadillo that can enclose itself completely in its shell. Unlike other armadillos, the sides of the shell are not connected to the skin. The rear section almost meets the shoulder section at midskirt. Hinging at this point, the fore and aft sections can be swung together like a clam shell, completely enclosing the animal with the top of the armored head and

The glyptodont was the formidable ancestor of today's armadillos. At right is a fossil skeleton with the shell in place, and on the opposite page is a skeleton without the shell.

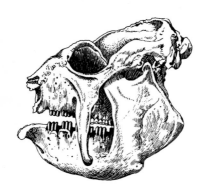

The skull of the glyptodont (drawing, above) had a remarkable bony prominence projecting downward from the cheek arch. The molars are somewhat like those of a rodent.

44

the tail stoppering the neck and tail notches. *T. matacus*, in a refinement of this action, leaves its shell partly agape; when touched on the abdomen, it slams the parts together like a steel trap. These animals are about 18 inches long, blackish-brown in color, and run with only the front clawtips touching the ground.

The genus *Dasypus* includes about five species of nine-banded armadillos. The typical species is *D. novemcinctus*. It is found from Missouri and Louisiana through Mexico into Central and South America. The chief characteristic is its shell, made up of small plates and divided usually into nine dorsal bands. The small, sturdy paws are almost wholly protected by the deep-skirted shell, which covers all but the feet, head and tail.

The usual color is brown, occasionally with dark spots. The head and body average length is about 17 inches. In Central and South America, the animal is hunted by means of traps placed at the entrances of dens. Although its flesh is edible and pleasant to the taste, it is sought especially for its shell, from which baskets and headgear are made.

The nine-banded armadillo lives in a deep den which can be described as an authentic masterpiece of engineering. From the entrance, a corridor runs perhaps 6 feet and then opens on a pit as much as 4 feet deep. At the bottom is a sort of living room where the armadillo spends a large part of its day. In the evening, it goes out in search of insects, small reptiles and amphibians, grunting and shambling rapidly about, pok-

The modern armadillo is a much less fearsome and brutish animal than its ancient antecedent. Its shell contains flexible joints, whereas the Glyptodont had a massive one-piece carapace. And of course it is much smaller.

ing its long snout into cracks and holes and piles of leaves. It usually prepares refuge dens in its habitual territory. If it does not have a prepared den nearby, it tries to escape an enemy by digging one wherever it happens to be.

All of the Dasypodids are noted for a reproductive peculiarity which has been widely studied. Each of their litters, which are born in February through April, are always of a single sex. This phenomenon is so well known that an old Brazilian ballad declares that the male has no sisters and the female

no brothers. The phenomenon is known to biologists as polyembryony. The entire litter (sometimes as many as eleven) is derived from a single fertilized egg. In the course of its development, the egg divides into nine to eleven parts, each of which becomes a little armadillo. Since sex is determined by the male sperm, it follows that as the fertilized egg divides, all division will have the same sex characteristic. Like identical twins in humans, they all share the same placenta.

Two genera of one species each are of considerable importance in the natural his-

The hairy armadillo (left) has stiff bristles growing sparsely between its bands, of which there are usually 18. If attacked it makes a snarling sound and tries to run or lowers its shell to the ground by drawing up its legs.

The giant armadillo (drawing below) has extremely powerful claws. It may grow to a weight of 130 pounds.

The pichi (bottom drawing) is a relative of the hairy armadillo. It makes its home in the Argentine pampas and Patagonia.

tory of the Dasypodidae: the **Lesser Pichiciego** (*Chlamyphorus truncatus*) and the **Greater Pichiciego** (*Burmeisteria retusa*). The lesser pichiciego is one of the rarest of animals. It lives in western Argentina, where it was virtually unknown, even to the local populations, until 1824, when it was discovered by Koming Harlan, an American naturalist. At 8 inches including tail, it is the smallest of the armadillos. The upper part of its body is covered by about 22 transverse plates of uniform width, all of them movable. The plates are anchored to two bony prominences above the eyes and to a narrow ridge of flesh along the spine. The rear of the animal is covered by a broad sort of butt plate which is anchored to the pelvic bones. When alarmed, this little armadillo may quickly burrow into the earth leaving the rear armor plate exposed like a bottle stopper. The limbs are short, strong and equipped with five long claws. The hind feet also have five toes.

This animal inhabits hot, sandy expanses in which it digs long tunnels leading to its den. It comes to the surface at night in search of insects. Only recently has it been possible to obtain a few specimens for scientific collections, and mostly these finds were

incidental to digging in land reclamation and irrigation.

The greater pichiciego is only slightly larger but differs also in its armor, which hangs down farther on the sides and adheres more to its body. It too lives in Bolivia and Argentina.

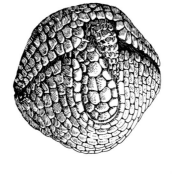

The three-banded arma-dillo (drawing right) walks usually with only the tips of its strong front claws touching the ground. When alarmed it can roll completely into a ball. In the rolled-up position the head is drawn back flush with the shell, and the tail fits neatly alongside it.

The lesser pichichiego (far right), is also called the fairy arma-dillo because it is tiny— only about 8 inches long —and generally delicate-looking. The shell is pale pink and extends only part way down the sides. The rest of the body and legs are covered with fine white hair. Its defense is to burrow swiftly into the sand and stopper the hole with its hind plate.

A 16th century drawing of a nine-banded arma-dillo (right) is a fairly good representation, ex-cept for the feet and claws, which are much too small.

Pholidota—
The Pangolins

The Pholidota, which at one time were classified with the order of the edentates, have often caused many disputes among scientists. Their anatomical organization is indeed strange and fascinating. These creatures look like great lizards, their upper parts being covered with a defensive armament of large horny scales.

The Pholidota roll themselves into balls if they are attacked. The scales then stand erect, their sharp cutting edges flared outward to discourage any assailant. The tail, which varies in length and is covered with similarly patterned scales, is convex at the top and flat at the bottom. But their "armor" is not the outstanding characteristic of the Pholidota—their most unusual structure is the tongue, which can be half as long as the whole body without the tail. Wormlike in appearance, the tongue has muscular roots that pass through the abdominal cavity and anchor to the pelvis. The organ has the same function as the anteater's tongue: coated with the glutinous secretion of the salivary glands, it is thrust into anthills and termitaries. The insects that adhere are withdrawn into the mouth and immediately swallowed.

The exterior ear canals of the pangolin can be completely shut; the nostrils too can be closed. The temporal and orbital cavities in the skull are not divided and the zygomatic arch is incomplete.

These remarkable characteristics naturally have aroused interest among students of evolution and comparative anatomy. Thus the Pholidota became the center of a dispute that persisted over some centuries. Today it is held that they constitute a special, isolated group among the mammals.

The order Pholidota embraces seven species, all members of one family, the Manidae,

Below, a baby pangolin hitches a ride on its mother's tail. This is the normal position for the young during their nursing period.

and a single genus, *Manis*. The order name is of Greek origin and means "clad in scales." The scales are unlike those of a reptile, which are flat and are connected all around. The pangolin's scales are attached on only one edge, and they overlap, much like those of a pine cone. Quite stiff and sharp, they can be raised at will. The sides of the face, throat and belly and the inside of the legs are bare, except for a few rigid hairs. The seven species can be subdivided into two major groups, the Asian and the African. In the Asian pangolins, the row of dorsal scales runs uninterrupted from the head to the tip of the tail. In the African species, this line is broken into two distinct series about two-thirds of the way along the body.

The Five-toed Pangolin (*Manis pentadactyla*), also called the Chinese pangolin, is typical of the Asian group. It has a few hairs between its scales, saw-toothed claws and no

A pangolin assumes its alert position (top photo). Then if it feels really threatened it rolls up into a tight and impervious ball. When in this position it can raise its sharp scales to further discourage a predator that might be inclined to cuff it around. The drawing below shows a cross section of a pangolin's scales. The scales actually are a modification of hair.

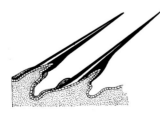

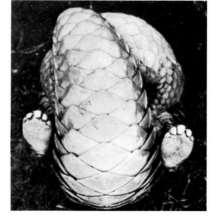

external ears to speak of. With its tail it reaches a length of some 4 feet. The eyes, which are small, protrude from the orbital cavity and are provided with sturdy lids. The mouth is small and toothless. The general lizardlike shape of the body is rather flattened. The sides of the forepaws rest on the ground, while the hind paws touch only the outer edge. The talons are particularly developed in the front, where they function as powerful digging tools.

The female has single births, although occasionally she may give birth to twins. The young have soft shells with flexible, moist scales. Within a few days, the air dries the scales and they become hard. During the nursing period, the young animal lives on the mother's back.

The pangolin is found in damp, equatorial forests. Predominantly nocturnal, it wanders slowly in search of anthills and termitaries, which it smashes with blows of its paws. Sometimes it walks on its hind legs, holding the forward part of its body erect.

The two other Asian species are closely related. The Indian pangolin (*Manis crassicaudata*), which lives in India and Ceylon, has a modest number of hairs among its scales. The Javanese pangolin (*M. javanica*) lives in southern Asia, Sumatra, Java, Borneo and the Philippines. In both species the length of the tail is only slightly less than the combined length of the head and body. The Chinese and Javanese pangolins occasionally climb trees, attaching themselves solidly with their claws and their prehensile tails.

Of the African group, the **Giant Pangolin** (*M. gigantea*) is the most typical representative. It can reach a length of 6 feet. Its tail is quite large, its legs are long and its armor is thick, composed of broad, sturdy scales. It too, with its strong claws, smashes anthills and termitaries and captures the insects with its tongue. When walking, the front claws

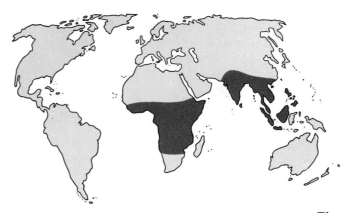

The colored areas of the map show the range of the various members of the Pholydotae, or pangolins.

The pangolin's brain (left) shows well developed olfactory lobes at the front and moderately convoluted hemispheres. The skull of the pangolin (below) has small eye cavities, the weak jaw of an anteater and no teeth at all.

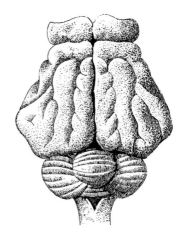

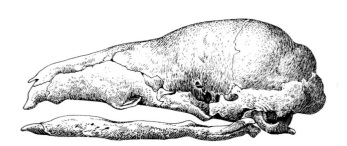

The Chinese called the pangolin "dragon carp." It is a rather mild and inoffensive beast to be called a dragon, although its shape could be called dragonlike, and the scales do suggest the large and coarse scales of a carp. In Africa it is sometimes called a "land crocodile." Although timid it is strong. When rolled up it is almost impossible to straighten out.

are held curved inward so that the weight falls on the padded outside edge of the paws. Like the others, the giant pangolin has no teeth, and it swallows masses of insects alive and whole. These are then "masticated" in certain horny, thick areas on the inner surface of the stomach. The pangolin swallows not only insects but also pebbles and mud, which contribute to the action.

Like all the other Pholydota, the giant pangolin can roll itself into a ball—the word

pangolin comes from the Malayan *pengguling*, meaning rolled into a ball. When rolled up it can raise its sharp scales and present a formidable defense to any enemy but man, who simply bashes it with a club. It is said, too, that if the pangolin is near a pool or a stream, it will plunge in and wait underwater, rolled in a ball, until the danger has passed—but this may be pure fiction.

The giant pangolin is found in central west Africa and especially in the Congo. It

Pangolin tails are clues to their identity. Of the top two drawings, the one on the left is an African species, and the one on the right is Asian. The middle drawing is of Manis Longicaudata, *and the bottom is* M. tricuspis.

was first described by the Roman naturalist, Claudius Aellanus, who mistook it for a reptile and spoke of it as a land crocodile. In every nation and time in which these animals have been known, pangolins have acquired strange appellations. To the Arabs it is "the father with the crust;" to the Indians, "the jungle fish;" to the Chinese, "the dragon carp." The Chinese once believed that many insects gathered among the pangolin's scales, to which they were attracted by its sweat,

and that the pangolin suddenly trapped and crushed them with its scales, and then ate them.

Our contemporary knowledge of the pangolin is only slightly greater than what was learned by the first observers who had the opportunity to examine them. According to H. Wendt, not even the Darwinians were able to make the slightest use of the "father with the crust" in demonstrating theories of evolution. They restricted themselves to de-

53

scribing the strange "masticatory apparatus" of these animals. Wilhelm Bolsche wrote a vivid description: "Its toothless mouth . . . does nothing but slobber like an old man's."

Zoological texts treat the pangolin as a rare "one-of-a-kind" animal because even today the precise relationship between this animal and other mammals is obscure. And so it will remain until new clues are discovered in the depths of geological strata.

The same area also has the tricuspid pangolin (*Manis tricuspis*). Its name derives from the peculiar design of its scales, which have a triple point.

Temminck's Pangolin (*Manis temmincki*) reaches a length of about 40 inches. The general color of its skin is blackish brown. The scales are yellow, very wide and rounded at the edge. While the giant, the long-tailed and the tricuspid pangolins often live in

The giant pangolin (right), can reach a length of 6 feet. It is extraordinarily strong, and is a truly impressive beast.

Another interesting African species is the **Long-tailed Pangolin** (*Manis longicaudata*). This form is characterized by the size of its tail, which accounts for two-thirds of its 3-foot length. In this species, therefore, the resemblance to a large lizard is especially prominent. The cranial skeleton possesses the various bone characteristics of the Pholydotae in much exaggerated form. There is no separation between the orbial and temporal cavities and no jugal bone, which makes the zygomatic arch incomplete.

In the long-tailed pangolin, as in all the species in the African group, two folds of the skin near the ear opening take the place of the external ear, at least in part. Whereas other pangolins have brown scales, the scales of this species are black with yellow edges. The animal lives in West Africa, in Senegal and Angola.

trees, Temminck's prefers the ground, along which it proceeds at a modest speed, holding its body in a semierect position.

Regardless of the care given to them. pangolins have never been able to survive more than two months in captivity because of the difficulty of acclimatization and because it is a problem to find enough insects to feed the animal. Every effort to train pangolins to other foods or artificial nutrients has failed.

Pangolins have come down to modern times from the Eocene virtually without major change. They represent a curious combination of very primitive characteristics (the skull structure) with a highly developed specialization of the tongue. In Asia and Africa, they occupy the same ecological niche held in America by the anteater, but like the armadillos they are armored mammals.

A long-tailed African tree pangolin heads for the high country. Although the enormously long tail is strong and prehensile, the pangolin relies mainly on its claws for a maneuver like this.

55

Lagomorpha— pikas, hares and rabbits

The science of animal classification, or taxonomy, has developed slowly over the past few hundred years, occasionally in an atmosphere of uncertainty and controversy. To classify an animal, tooth formation, arrangement and structure must be considered. So too are the skeletal structure, skull shape, digestive system, method of locomotion, body covering, number and function of the digits, blood proteins and fossil ancestry. But the natural sciences are not mathematically exact and frequently conclusions depend on the opinions of the most respected authorities.

A case in point is the lagomorphs—pikas, hares and rabbits—which long were classified as rodents because their teeth are basically similar, as is their general way of life.

But these animals have two pairs of upper incisors—that is, a small pair of incisors grow behind the large main pair—whereas this does not occur in any of the other rodents. So the rodents were divided into two suborders: the Duplicidentata (pikas, hares and rabbits) and the Simplicidentata (all others).

But further distinctions were pointed out. The jaw articulation of the Duplicidentata permits side-to-side motion for grinding food between the molars, whereas the other rodents grind food with a back-and-forth motion. The digestive systems differed—lagomorphs have a fold in the caecum, the sac at the upper end of the colon, which is lacking in the others. But the clincher was to be found in the blood proteins. The blood serum of the lagomorphs was clearly different from that of the rest of the rodents—in fact it more closely resembled the type found in ungulates. Today zoologists recognize the Lagomorpha as a separate order.

The wild mouse (top photo and drawing) has a typical rodent's skull and tooth arrangement. It has enormous incisors and the characteristic diastema, the wide empty space between the incisors and the molars.

The wombat (Vombatus ursinus, lower photo) is a marsupial. This vegetarian has a skull structure (drawing, far right) similar to a rodent.

The Old World rabbit Oryctolagus cuniculus (opposite page) has a grayish-brown coat which aids in camouflaging it as protection from its enemies.

Oryctolagus, *the domestic rabbit (below) has a skull structure with a high, narrow frontal bone and large orbital cavities, which are typical of Lagomorphs. Rabbits, hares and picas also have a second pair of small upper incisors which are lacking in rodents.*

The Greek word Lagomorpha means "hare-shaped." In a sense this means that a hare is called a hare because it looks like a hare. A distinguishing characteristic is the additional set of small incisors mentioned above. These small incisors have enamel on both sides, whereas the big incisors have it only on the forward side. The main upper incisors are quite visible in the Lagomorpha because the upper lip is deeply slotted (hence the term "hare lip" as applied to the human defect). Incisor teeth are thus six in all, because there are two others in the mandible. Total dentition in the Lagomorpha varies from 26 to 28. Being herbivorous, lagomorphs have a large empty space between the incisors and the premolars, called the diastema. The incisors are evergrowing, but

constant gnawing keeps them worn to the proper length. If one tooth is broken, the opposing one, having nothing to wear against, will continue to grow in an arc, even to the point of curling back and piercing the roof of the mouth. The roots are open and extend deep into the skull and jawbone.

Lagomorphs, strictly vegetarian, have a highly developed intestine and a large stomach. These animals have a remarkable way of getting the most from their diet of leaves and grass. Their feces consists of two types of pellets: moist ones and dry ones. The moist pellets are later swallowed so that the food is digested twice. Presumably this recovers some of the vitamins manufactured by the bacteria of the lower intestine that would otherwise be lost. Other distinguish-

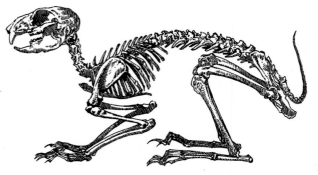

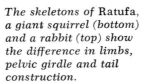

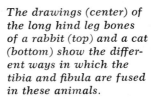

The skeletons of Ratufa, a giant squirrel (bottom) and a rabbit (top) show the difference in limbs, pelvic girdle and tail construction.

The drawings (center) of the long hind leg bones of a rabbit (top) and a cat (bottom) show the different ways in which the tibia and fibula are fused in these animals.

A skull X-ray of Hydrochoerus hydrochaeris, the capybara (far left), illustrates the enormous incisors with the open roots set deeply into the cranium.

The drawing (far left, bottom) shows the smooth hemispheres of the rabbit's brain.

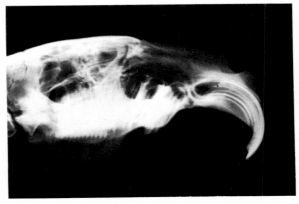

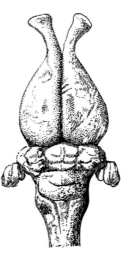

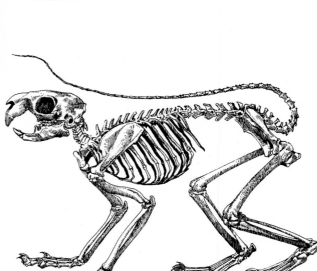

ing characteristics include the long, mobile ears (except in pikas) and the short, up-turned tail. A pouch behind the cheeks allows food storage once the animal is satiated. The forelimbs are short; the hind limbs are long, robust and well adapted for swift running with extended leaps.

The Lagomorpha are distributed widely, though they are few in South America and were imported into Australia; as a result they are today found almost worldwide. The sexual ardor of the males is quite impressive and the females are extremely prolific, with several large litters each year. The young are born helpless but develop very rapidly. The testicles of the males are unusual in that they are located in a scrotum in front of the penis.

Lagomorphs are heavily preyed upon by carnivores and raptors and are avidly hunted by men, but their shrewd and speedy

The rock cony or pica Ochotona princeps (above) is often called a whistling hare owing to the whistle-like bark which the animal emits as a warning.

Ochotona, the collared pica (right), is a small, grayish animal that lives in the cold, bleak mountains of Alaska and the Yukon.

escape reflexes and high rate of reproduction has enabled the various species to thrive.

Fossil finds show that the origins of the Lagomorpha go back some 55,000,000 years to the Upper Paleocene in Eurasia and America. One of the three families into which the order is divided, the Eurymylidae, is exclusively fossil. There are two living families, the Ochotonidae and the Leporidae.

Ochotonidae—the pikas

Pikas are sometimes known as whistling hares, because of the high-pitched warning cry that they send out as they dive for their burrows. They are also variously called rock rabbits, mouse hares, haymakers, and conies. They resemble guinea pigs. They are slightly smaller than the general run of hares and rabbits and are distinguished by their short, broad ears and the nearly equal length of forelimbs and hind limbs. The head is rather big, and the tiny tail is hidden by fur. The dentition includes 26 teeth—six incisors, ten premolars, ten molars; the upper incisors are grooved in front. The family includes a single living genus, indigenous for the most part to cold climates. Sometimes they live in large groups. They do not hibernate in winter and consequently during the growing season they work hard at gathering and storing food. They are found in Asia, in North America, and in parts of eastern Europe.

Asian Pikas (*Ochotona pusilla*), the pikas of the steppes, measure 7 to 7½ inches in length. Their pelage, or fur, is a rather dark, uniform gray, with black ears edged in white. This is a graceful little animal with a short, stubby body; it is the only species among all the Ochotonidae which is native to the European continent. Before the onset of cold weather it puts away a good store of grasses in rocky ravines or in depressions in the soil. The pika's haystack often reaches a height of 3 feet. Then it digs a burrow from its nest to the store, to be used when the ground is covered with snow. Its preferred environment is the steppe, where it lives in large groups. A total vegetarian, the pika works at night or during cloudy days; it rests during the hottest, sunniest hours of the day. *O. pusilla* is found in Europe in the Volga basin and eastward through Siberia. Russian farmers and sable hunters seek out the pika's haystack to use as fodder for farm animals or for the hunter's horses. The pika, thus deprived of its winter store, starves to death.

The Cony or American Pika (*Ochotona princeps*), indigenous to the mountains of the American West, is about the same size as the others, reaching a length of up to 10 inches. Its distinguishing characteristics are the rather big snout and the short, broad ears, kept in constant movement to pick up the slightest sound. The coloring of the fur varies considerably, depending on its locale. It may range from gray to reddish to ochre, with the underparts lighter than the back.

The cony is a fine runner and jumper. It also is a great storer of leaves and grasses, which it first cures in the sun and then stores in the fissures of rocks. This busy work is performed during the day, except for a long siesta in the sun. From time to time the cony emits its characteristic whistling cry.

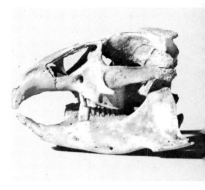

The forepart of the fossilized skull above shows it is from the Ochotonidae family.

The Afghan pica (above) is one of the twelve species native to Asia. They usually live where the winters are long and severe, but they do not hibernate.

The colored areas of the map show the distribution of Ochotonidae in Asia and America. One species is found in eastern Europe near the Caspian Sea.

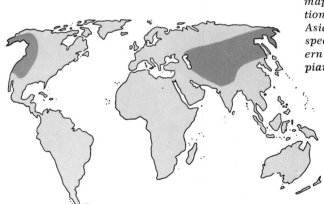

The European hare Lepus europaeus (below) prefers to escape danger by "freezing" with the help of camouflage, but when obliged to flee from a predator it can speed up to 45 miles per hour.

In the coldest months the animal remains in a burrow, emerging only to feed from its store. The reproductive period lasts from spring until the first snow. The maximum litter is four young. After about two weeks these are ready to lead an independent life, and the female prepares for a second and later a third pregnancy.

To the north, the distribution of the cony meets that of the **Alaskan Collared Pika** (*O. collaris*), which is smaller, but otherwise similar.

Leporidae— the hares and rabbits

This is the other, much larger, family in the order Lagomorpha. There are 9 genera and about 50 species. Most of their characteristics have been brought out in the general discussion of lagomorphs. Hares and rabbits are frequently confused. The Belgian hare, for example, is not a hare but a variety of the domestic rabbit, and the American jackrabbits are actually true hares. Hares are generally larger, lankier and longer-eared than rabbits. Hares do not burrow, but simply nest in a ground depression, whereas rabbits dig elaborate tunnels and chambers. Hare babies are born open-eyed, active and fully furred; rabbit young are born blind and naked. In the United States no distinction is commonly made between hares and rabbits. They are all simply called rabbits.

The tracks of both are distinctive. They never walk or trot, but hop or leap. When moving slowly the front feet are placed one in front of the other and the hind feet are brought up together and put down side by side in front of the front feet. When they run fast, the basic pattern remains the same, but with a greater interval.

Rabbits are of great economic importance. Sometimes they are destroyers of grass and crops, particularly in areas where their natural predators have been killed off, or when they are introduced to a land that has no effective predators. But they are an important source of food and clothing. Rabbits have been raised for their meat since Roman times, and wild rabbits were hunted for tens of thousands of years before that. Today they are far and away the most hunted game

Fossils of several existing genera date back 30 million years; with such an ancient

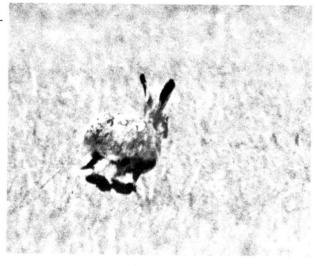

This drawing of the skull of a hare shows three premolars and three molars on each side.

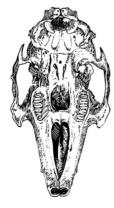

heritage and today's worldwide distribution, it is surprising that the various Leporidae are so much alike.

Some 200 species of hares are included in the genus *Lepus*, but probably this number should be reduced because some may be only subspecies. We must limit ourselves to mentioning only a few chosen from among the many found throughout the world.

The European Hare (*Lepus europaeus*)—the very name suggests images of agility, speed

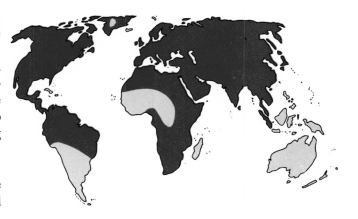

The colored areas on the map indicate the almost universal distribution of Leporidae. Picas, hares and rabbits are found worldwide except in Australia, Malagasy, South America and west central Africa.

The Cape hare Lepus capensis (left) prefers the open ranges but may occasionally be found in evergreen forests.

The partly reconstructed skeleton of Paleolagus, an extinct Lagomorph, has the typical tooth arrangement of a rabbit.

and tremendous leaps. When pursued it employs a technique of fleeing not in a straight line but in unpredictably varied tacks, recrossing its own path, running along a hedge in one direction, then rounding the end and returning on the opposite side, always with the clear objective of confusing the pursuer. It may also flatten itself down into depressions in the terrain when danger threatens.

The European hare varies in length from 27 to 29 inches, of which 3 to 4 inches are tail. The small head and neck are quite distinct from the body, the snout is rounded, the eyes are large and bright, and the ears long (up to 5½ inches). The rear part of the body is particularly strong, and this strength combined with the length of the legs permits the animal to achieve leaps of 15 feet or more and to attain bursts of speed up to 45 miles per hour. Like others of its genus, it has 28 teeth, with the incisors prominently visible through the upper lip slot.

The European hare does not burrow, nesting rather in small holes or depressions in

The European hare is born with its eyes open and begins to care for itself after about two weeks. The hare does not burrow but makes grass-lined nests in depressions in the ground.

64

the terrain. It is active in the evening and at night. Its diet consists of vegetation found in fields and meadows. It has the custom of rising on its hind limbs to look about, at the same time beating its forepaws together. When alarmed it pricks up its ears, which are lowered when running. Its voice, which is a kind of murmuring, is rarely heard, except in mating season, when it is quite distinct. The female has three or four litters a summer after a gestation of about one month. The young, which number from two to four, are weaned at about 15 days; after 40 days they live independently of the parents. The males generally outnumber the females, and in the mating season battle fiercely, with biting, scratching and tearing out of fur.

This species is found throughout all of

Hares are the food supply for many fur-bearing carnivores. Where conditions are ideal, hares become abundant and foxes, lynxes, weasels and mink thrive. Hares also fall prey to larger hawks and owls.

central and southern Europe, as far south as the Mediterranean and the Caucasus. It is only when the hare population grows out of proportion that the species becomes harmful to the farmer, eating his clover, medicinal herbs and green wheat. Today man and the hare's natural enemies, the fox, weasel, hawk, etc., keep the species reduced.

The Blue Hare, Mountain Hare, or European Varying Hare (*Lepus timidus* or *L. variabilis*), is the type species of Lepus, the one most representative of the genus. In summer it resembles the European hare except that it is somewhat smaller, averaging about 20 to 24 inches in length, not counting the 2½-inch tail.

The name "varying hare" comes from the color of the fur, which changes according to

the season. During the summer the thick, soft fur is brownish-gray, sometimes tending toward reddish. The underparts, the limbs, the tail, a circle around the eyes, the edge of the ears (except for the tips, which are black) are all either white or whitish. During winter, the fur turns white; nothing of the rabbit can be seen against the snow but the black-tipped ears.

The species is indigenous to the Pyrenees, the Alps, the Caucasus, Iceland, Scotland,

The Alpine hare Lepus alpinus *(below) and the European hare,* Lepus europaeus, *have the long ears, legs and tail which distinguishes them from rabbits.*

The three to four young hares produced in each litter are hidden in dense vegetation, singly or in pairs, and visited by their mother for nursing. One of the hare's best defenses against predators is its ability to stay absolutely motionless or flatten itself against the ground when danger threatens. Its grayish-brown fur makes it practically undetectable.

Scandinavia, northern Europe and northern Asia as far as Japan. The cry of the varying hare consists of puffing and hissing sounds. One cry, a characteristic "hoo-hoo" sound, is emitted only during the mating season.

The Snowshoe Rabbit or Varying Hare (*Lepus americanus*) derives its name from the hind

Sharing its environment with the tireless hunters of Europe, the hare (Lepus europaeus) has had to develop techniques for staying alive. These include an incredible talent for running, jumping and evasion—as well as the almost perfect ability to disappear against the green-brown coloring of the field or forest background, as shown at left.

The white-tailed jackrabbit, Lepus townsendi, *is not a rabbit at all, but a hare. With its long, strong hind legs it can outrun and outmaneuver a fox or coyote.*

The antelope jackrabbit, Lepus alleni *(opposite page, far right), and the California jackrabbit,* Lepus californicus *(opposite page, left), are two species of the genus* Lepus *found in the western United States and Canada.*

The snowshoe rabbit (opposite page, lower left) displays its summer coat of gray and tan fur. This species is so named because its hind feet are broad and well adapted for walking in the snow. Its winter coat (opposite page, lower right) is white for camouflage in the snow.

feet, which are adapted for easy travel over soft snow. During the winter the hairs on the feet lengthen and thicken, and as the rabbit hops it spreads its toes wide. The combined effect is that of a snowshoe. It is rather smaller than the European hare, with relatively short ears. In winter it is snow white, in the summer brown. The snowshoe rabbit has cycles of great abundance and scarcity. Over a period of about 10 years, the population builds up until they may be 5,000 to the square mile. Then a devastating plague strikes, killing them by the millions. After the spring snow-melt their wasted bodies lie strewn across the floor of the northern Canadian forest.

The Arctic Hare (*Lepus arcticus*) is indigenous to the northernmost reaches of the American continent. Stocky and heavy, the Arctic hare is a giant among lagomorphs, sometimes attaining a length of 30 inches. It has short ears, probably to conserve body heat during the long, bitter winters. In sum-

mer its coat is predominantly silvery gray, and white on the belly. The winter coat is pure white, with only the ear tips black. The brief duration of the mild season in the Arctic allows only a single litter each year.

The White-tailed Jackrabbit (*Lepus townsendi*) is large, strong and very fast—it can lope along easily at 35 miles per hour and spurt to 45, covering 18 to 20 feet at a leap. It eats any green vegetation and particularly likes alfalfa. The coyote is its normal predator, but coyote poisoning programs have resulted in runaway jackrabbit populations with much destruction of farming and grazing lands. The bucks fight furiously in the mating season. Litters of four to eight young are born in a simple grass-lined nest beneath a bush or clump of grass. The young nurse for a few days, then begin gradually to forage for themselves, becoming independent in three or four weeks. White-tailed jackrabbits have been observed in a sort of ritual dance. A dozen or so will form a large circle, then

gradually close in toward the center. At a certain point they all bounce into the air and scamper off, only to repeat the performance a few minutes later. Their range is the American Northwest and British Columbia. During the summer the coat is buff; in winter it is white all over except for the ear tips, which are black year round.

One species of the cotton-tail is Sylvilagus audu-boni *which has short, very soft fur.*

The Black-tailed Jackrabbit (*Lepus californicus*) has enormous ears, long and broad, and a rather long tail, which droops rather than stands erect. Like the other jackrabbits, it is not a rabbit but a hare. The name "jackrabbit" is a contraction of "jackass rabbit," in reference to its generally long-eared, gangly and bony appearance. Its legs are strongly developed. It attains a length of 28 inches and over. Several times a year the female has a litter of seven or eight young which quickly become independent. This incredible prolificacy often leads to drastic destruction of crops. It is consequently the object of intensive hunting, often with bounties. Harney County, Oregon, alone has paid bounties on more than one million tails in a single year. It ranges from Washington east to Nebraska and south into Mexico. The black-tailed jack is unmistakable, with its buff brown coat, huge ears tipped with black, and its pendant black tail.

The remaining species of the Lagomorpha are those known by the general but useful term *rabbits*, which at least serves to distinguish them from hares. Rabbits are shorter-eared, shorter-legged and smaller than hares. The ear tips are never black.

The Cottontail (genus *Sylvilagus*) is the common rabbit found throughout the Americas from Alaska to Patagonia, though sparsely in lower South America. There are about five major species, all of which are fairly similar. This is the American Easter bunny, the "Br'er Rabbit" of Uncle Remus' tales, and the

appealing "Thumper" of Walt Disney. The Easter rabbit concept probably stemmed from pre-Christian times. An old Teutonic legend tells of a bird that was changed into a rabbit by Ostara, the goddess of Spring. Grateful for the transmogrification, the rabbit (or hare) laid eggs at the festival of Ostara in April—or Easter, as the goddess' name-day has come down to us.

The cottontail is 15 inches long at best and has short broad ears and soft fur that ranges from gray through tan. Altogether it is less bony and angular than the larger hares. The tail, white underneath and held erect, is perfectly described by the rabbit's common name. It may appear that a target animal such as the rabbit violates evolutionary laws by flashing such a bright signal when chased —a less visible rear end might serve it better.

Young eastern cottontails (Sylvilagus floridanus) often huddle together in dense brush for protection against their natural enemies, wolves, coyotes, rattlesnakes and man.

A baby cottontail instinctively stays put while its mother is away. Here one has been put on the head of a large dog, where it remained immobile until removed.

71

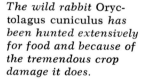
But probably the rabbit with the most visible tail was followed by other startled rabbits. Likely Tail-end Charlie would then be caught, not the leader with the bright signal.

Cottontails feed chiefly at dusk or at night, but they may be active at any time of day. Brushy country is preferred by most types, but some species take to the swamps—all are excellent swimmers.

Normally timorous, a mother cottontail will fight if her babies are threatened in the nest. Biting and kicking frantically, she is quite capable of driving off a large snake or even a raccoon double her weight. Depending on the length of the warm season, she may deliver as many as five litters a year, each fathered by a different buck. Births occur in an underground chamber which the mother lines with fur torn from her breast.

Cottontails are hunted relentlessly by foxes, wildcats, coyotes, badgers, eagles, dogs and people. Tens of millions are killed each year by hunters, yet they thrive, busily nibbling grass in the meadows, woodlands and plains, the alfalfa and vegetables of farms and the lawns and gardens of the suburbs.

The Domestic or Old World Rabbit (*Oryctolagus cuniculus*) is most common in the Mediterranean region of Europe and North Africa. It has shorter ears and legs than the hare. The average length is from 15 to 18 inches, not counting the 2-inch tail.

Reports of grave crop damage by rabbits go back many centuries. The damage was so serious in the Balearic Islands at one point that a petition was sent to the Emperor Augustus for help in fighting the animals. In much more recent times the wild rabbit

The wild rabbit Oryctolagus cuniculus *has been hunted extensively for food and because of the tremendous crop damage it does.*

has committed incalculable damage in several countries, most notably in Australia, where a few specimens were imported around 1820. It is estimated that the descendants of those few rabbits had become 13 or 14 *million* in only a few years. Hunting did not keep the rabbit population down (the single state of Victoria exported almost 40 million skins between 1877 and 1889), and wire net fences proved equally futile.

The mating season for this rabbit lasts all during the mild season. Litters are delivered at about 40-day intervals. Each litter includes from five to twelve young, born naked and blind. After about three weeks of nursing they quickly become independent; full adulthood is reached at about ten months. The female lines a part of the burrow with fur from her own chest, belly and flanks. The nests are a complicated series of tunnels with various exits, ventilation holes and a main chamber. The diet consists of grass, roots, sprouts and bark.

When it feels in danger (and only then) the wild rabbit emits a kind of murmuring cry. It also beats its hind limbs heavily and repeatedly against the ground. Cold and humidity are among its enemies, and an epidemic sickness, myxomatosis.

Anatomically the Old World rabbit does not differ from the wild rabbit, but the breeding to which it has been subjected for several centuries has produced a number of types which for the most part no longer resemble their wild ancestors. Some are bred for quality of fur, others for meat, still others for sporting activities.

The white giant rabbit is one of the most attractive domestic breeds of Oryctolagus. It is used as a pet, a show rabbit and in laboratory experiments.

73

Rodentia— The Rodents

Rats and mice are rodents. But so are agoutis, beavers, capybaras, cavies, chipmunks, chinchillas, coruros, gerbils, guinea pigs, gundies, hutias, hamsters, jerboas, lemmings, marmots, muskrats, pacas, porcupines, prairie dogs, sewellels, springhares, squirrels, tuco-tucos, tuzas, voles, woodchucks and a few more. In all there are probably close to 2,400 species, living and extinct. There is no way to check, of course, but it is a fair guess that there are more individual rodents alive today than all other mammals added together.

Practically every land area of the world is host to some kind of rodent, and several species have spread worldwide, in some cases by stowing away on men's ships and boats.

Rodents live in fields, mountains, plains, deserts, swamps, trees, lakes, sewers, riverbanks, houses, barns, churches and warehouses. Some rodents shuffle. Others walk, run, leap, climb, burrow, swim on or under the water and fly—or, more precisely, glide. They vary in length from 2½ inches to almost 4 feet, and in weight from 1½ ounces to 100 pounds.

Rodents are gnawing mammals with 2 incisors in each jaw. These teeth are long and enameled only on the outer side. The roots are hollow and the teeth grow from the roots outward in long arcs throughout the animal's life. The incisors are constantly honed against each other to maintain a chisel edge, and thus they are kept at a proper length. Canines are absent and there is a space, the diastema, between the incisors

Gerbils (opposite page) are native to Africa, particularly North Africa, and southern Asia. They are burrowing rodents, mainly nocturnal and vegetarian, with a head and body length of 4 to 6 inches. Gerbils have recently become popular as pets. The Cape short-eared gerbil shown here seems to thrive in captivity and is quite docile when handled, though it will fight and kill any smaller rodents caged with it.

A hibernating dormouse (above) lies curled up amid empty acorn shells. Before its six month sleep it also fattened on seeds and fruits.

In summer the dormouse holes up during the day and emerges from its nest (at left) to forage at night.

The pig-sized capybara (far left) is a giant among rodents. These animals are hunted by South American natives, who eat their flesh and make ornaments of their large teeth.

The desert Jerboa (Jaculus orientalis, below) hops like a kangaroo and uses its long, tufted tail as a support when standing. It is nocturnal and quite shy and agile. With a body length of only 4 or 5 inches it nevertheless moves rapidly over the ground in leaps several yards long. Jerboas seldom drink. Instead they obtain whatever water they need from their diet of seeds, grasses, bulbs and roots.

and the premolars. The typical dental formula is $I^{1/1}$, $C^{0/0}$, $Pm^{2/1}$, $M^{3/3}$.

Most rodents have four functioning toes on each front foot and five on each hind foot. They walk on their whole front foot and on the ball and toes of the hind foot, with the heel held low. In some species the forelimbs are adapted to grasping and holding food while feeding. This capability usually coincides with highly developed hind limbs. The tail varies widely among the species. It may be long or short, flat, round, or conical, bare or covered with hair or scales. The tails of some groups are built to break off if grabbed,

which serves as an escape device for the rest of the animal. Normally the whiskers and other vibrissae are highly developed. In spite of size and functional differences among rodents, they all share a very similar structure. The radius and ulna in the forelimbs are distinct, permitting free and rotary movement of the front feet. Often the tibia and fibula in the hind limbs are used. The nervous system is unremarkable, the brain usually having smooth hemispheres with occasional convolutions.

The digestive system of rodents is distinctive. Cheek pouches, either internal or external, store food to be eaten later. The stomach of some rodents is small and simple. In others it is divided into two sections. The first is for storage; the second section contains the digestive glands.

The testicles are carried either in the abdomen or groin and usually descend temporarily during the breeding period. The female of some groups has a double uterus. The mammary glands are thoracic or abdominal and from two to twelve in number. In some aquatic species there may be as many as 20 mammary glands placed on the flanks or near the back. The anal scent glands begin functioning only with sexual maturity, and may be accompanied by other glands in other parts of the body.

Almost all rodents are highly prolific. In the males the sexual instinct is very strong, and the females become repeatedly pregnant during the warm part of the year. The babies are usually born in burrows or well constructed nests lined with grass. In almost all species the young develop rapidly. Rodents unquestionably contribute to the general balance of nature by supplying sustenance to carnivores, raptors and reptiles, but their exuberant breeding can develop into a huge problem, both for themselves and their environment, when their predators are eliminated.

Rodents generally lead nocturnal lives.

They are almost all very timid animals, usually surprisingly agile, sometimes lazy and somnolent. They have an indisputable relationship to man's economy since they are destroyers of agricultural crops against whom an unceasing battle must be waged; yet they supply valuable fur. Their flesh is generally considered by humans to be overly sharp and disagreeable. But some squirrels are delicious.

The services rendered to man by rodents in research laboratories are incalculable. White mice and guinea pigs have played an essential role in medical research, to the point where "guinea pig" became a collo-

Burrowing rodents of arid areas are usually earth-colored and unmarked by stripes or spots. This scheme blends well with the ground and makes it difficult for predators to spot them. Their fur is usually short, dense, and smooth so that dust and dirt brushes off readily.

The Old World red squirrel, Scuirus vulgaris (bottom), is a fearless and highly excitable creature when fighting for a mate or protecting its young. Squirrels are often the subject of European folklore tales and are connected with the ancient gods of mythology and legend. In Germany, squirrels were believed to be "the little people of the trees," closely related to elves.

77

quial term meaning an individual who willingly or unwillingly undergoes experimental tests.

Classification of rodents is highly complex and not free from controversy. There are 35 families and 351 genera composed of about 2,400 species. Some scholars group the families into three suborders: Sciuromorpha (squirrels, chipmunks, beavers, etc.), Myomorphia (rats, mice, lemmings, gerbils, etc.) and Hystricomorpha (porcupines, guinea pigs, chinchillas, mole rats, etc.) In this book, however, we will ignore the suborder classi-

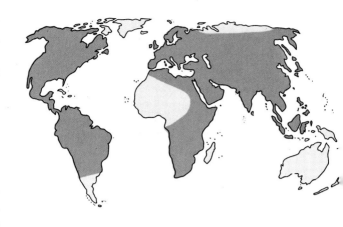

fications and simply put the families and significant genera in logical sequence.

Aplodontida—The Sewellels

This family has a single species, the sewellel (*Aplondontia Rufa*). This animal is sometimes known as the mountain beaver, though it is not a beaver at all and has no preference for mountains. It measures about 16 inches long, including its stub tail. It is a stocky animal, with a broad, flat head and short legs. It has 22 teeth with unrooted molars and premolars. Its color is grayish-brown with a lighter underside. The eyes are small. The sewellel is indigenous to North America (British Columbia, the Sierra Nevadas and northern California). It is a fair climber, with feet well adapted to this activity, and frequently goes aloft to nip off tender shoots and small branches. It digs

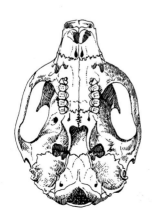

extremely complex tunnels, preferably in wet soil near streams, and is active mostly at dusk. Mating takes place in the spring; the litter includes two or three blind and nearly hairless young. Sewellels are hunted for their fur and meat.

Sciuridae—
The Squirrel Family

This family includes about 50 genera, distributed throughout the world except for Australia, Madagascar, southern South America and the deserts of Arabia and Egypt. They range in size from the 7-ounce tropical pygmy squirrel to the 7-pound marmot.

The Old World Red Squirrel (*Sciurus vulgaris*) measures about 10 inches in length, with a tail of about 6½ to 8½ inches long. Distinguishing features are the quick, agile body; a broad forehead, somewhat flattened; large, slightly protruding eyes and broad ears with a tuft of hair at the tip. The tail is richly furred and held curled over the back.

Tree squirrels seldom harm the woods because they normally do no damage to the bark. Hazelnus, walnuts and the seeds of fir, beech and maple make up their diet. In bad times they may eat shoots, tender leaves and small plants extensively. But squirrels are plunderers of nests, eating both eggs and small birds. They store provisions for the winter (the red squirrel does not hibernate), keeping them near the nest, which is usually high in the fork of a tree or in a hollow trunk. The nest is round and made of grass, twigs, pieces of bark and lined with moss. After a 40-day gestation period the female gives birth from two to four times a year, with three to six tiny, naked young in each litter. The young are blind at birth and remain so for 30 days, but become independent at about two months. The red squirrel is found in the wooded sections of Europe, northern Asia, Japan and northern China.

The Gray Squirrel (*Sciurus carolinensis*) is among the best known American mammals. Sometimes called the cat squirrel or black squirrel, it is found in hardwood forests from Canada to Florida and as far west as Minnesota. It reaches a length of about 20 inches, nearly half of which is its round, bushy tail, which can be wrapped around the body to retain heat, or used to balance the squirrel in its aerial leaps. The fur is rusty-gray above

The gray squirrel is most active in the early morning and late afternoon and lives to be about 15 years old. When food is scarce, gray squirrels will devour everything edible, then migrate. An extraordinary migration of gray squirrels, from Wisconsin to Minnesota, took place in 1905 and necessitated crossing the Mississippi River. Readily tamed, the gray squirrel is common today even in cities, where it is familiar in parks

The sun squirrel (opposite page) derives its name from a fondness for basking on tree branches in the tropical sun.

The fox squirrel (left), the New World gray squirrel (far left) and the tassel-eared squirrel (bottom left) adopt their characteristic feeding stance, sitting on their hind legs and grasping food in their forepaws.

Paraxerus, the South African bush squirrel (below), is a tree squirrel which spends most of its time high in the branches and descends only to forage for food.

and paler on the underside. The ears are erect and pointed, the eyes full and bright. Their diet consists of nuts, preferably hickory; acorns, seeds and shoots, which are accumulated during the autumn and buried or deposited in the crevices of trees. The spherical nest of twigs, leaves and bark is built in the fork of a tall tree. Cavities of trees serve as storm shelters and as nurseries. The three to four young, born usually in June, may remain in the parent nest for one year.

and public gardens, and accepts food from visitors without timidity. The western variety of the gray squirrel is *Sciurus griseus*. It is larger than its eastern counterpart, about 22 inches, with a broad tail in which the dominant gray has tawny and yellowish nuances.

The Fox Squirrel (*Sciurus niger*) is 10 to 15 inches long, with a 9- to 14-inch tail. Its color varies with location. In the northern states it is usually yellowish-rust above and pale yellow to orange below. In the south it is gray with a dark head, white nose and ears. The fox squirrel has a heavy body and a square face. It prefers to live in oak and pine groves, borders of cypress swamps and thickets. It makes a shrill barking noise and can make its teeth chatter. The fox squirrel lives for about ten years. It is closely related to *S. apache* and *S. arizonensis* of Mexico and Arizona and the tuft-eared or tassel-eared squirrel *S. aberti*.

The North American Red Squirrel or Chickaree (*Tamiasciurus hudsonicus*) is among the smaller squirrels, only 16 inches long. The fur is tawny or brown on top, with yellowish or reddish tints, and white below. The two colors are divided by a distinct stripe. Its ears usually have a tuft at the tip in winter. It is active in the daytime and on nights with a full moon, when its drawn-out vibrant call can often be heard. Other times it chatters and jabbers excitedly, and when annoyed goes into a real frenzy, complete with sputterings and foot-stamping. It is capable of jumping gracefully from limb to limb, but spends much of its time on the ground. It nests in trees, either in a fork or hollow trunk, and digs burrows in the ground which serve as refuges from pursuers. It spends the coldest days of winter in its nest, living on stored provisions. It does not hibernate. The female bears three to four young in the spring. The chickaree is native to Alaska and Canada, but

The marmot (left and far left) favors the temperate regions of the United States, Canada, Europe and parts of Siberia, where it lives in burrows or in dens among rocks.

The hoary marmot Marmota caligata (below) is watchful of intruders in its home territory. When danger approaches, the marmot sounds a whistling signal made in the back of its throat without any movement of its lips.

may be found as far south as the heavily forested parts of the Carolinas. It lives to be nine years old. A closely related species is *T. douglasi.*

The Indian Palm Squirrel (*Funambulus*) is 5 to 7 inches long with an equally long tail. Its long fur is grayish-brown above with three parallel stripes on its flanks and white below. It lives in the Indo-Malayan region, where its small whistling cries can be heard daily by the natives.

The Brush Squirrel (*Paraxerus*) is native to South Africa. It is similar to *Sciurus vulgaris* in dimensions and behavior. Another African genus is *Heliosciurus,* which includes seven species.

The Black-eared Squirrel (*Nannosciurus whiteheadi*) lives in Borneo and measures only 3 to 4 inches long, excluding the tail.

The short, soft fur is olive gray to dark red-dish-brown It is a mountain tree squirrel; the various species of the genus are known as "oriental pygmy squirrels."

The otherwise agile squirrel family includes the ground-dwelling marmot. The marmot, whose name means mountain mouse, is a squat, stocky and clumsy animal. These somewhat languid creatures eat herbaceous vegetation during the day and retire to their burrows for the night. These burrows are usually found in well drained soil or among large rocks and have several entrances. It is not uncommon for two to four marmots to hibernate together, their body temperature staying between 43 and 57° F.

About 16 species are distributed across the cooler parts of the northern hemisphere.

The Yellow-bellied Marmot (*Marmota fla-viventris*) lives in the Black Hills of South Dakota and in Wyoming. It is 14 to 19 inches long with a 9-inch tail and weighs about 10 pounds. It is a grizzled yellowish-brown above with a black face and yellow undersides.

The Hoary Marmot (*Marmota caligata*) lives in the mountains of the American North-west. It is sometimes called the whistler because of its shrill, high-pitched call, which can be heard a mile away through the clear mountain air. Its coat is marbled with black and white. During the day it eats grasses, hay and roots. Its den is burrowed as deep as 20 feet below the surface of the ground. These dens have long corridors leading off the main one, with several exits. After a gestation period of about five weeks, two to four young are born and nursed for about 40 days. They are capable of reproduction at the age of two years. Their whistlelike voices become grunts when they are angry.

The Woodchuck or Ground Hog (*Marmota monax*) is the smallest American marmot. Its diet consists of clover, alfalfa and fragrant grasses, on which it fattens itself in preparation for its hibernation from December to March. The woodchuck's burrow contains several chambers and usually three exits: front, back and drop hole. This last opening is a straight shaft going down two

or more feet, next to which the woodchuck may sit observing an approaching intruder until the last moment, when it drops out of sight into the safety of its burrow.

Ground Hog Day, February 2nd, is the day when Mr. Ground Hog traditionally pops out to check the weather. If it is cloudy, it means an early spring; a sunny day means six more weeks of cold. This belief traces back to an old European tradition in which the hedge-

hog and badger do the weather forecasting on the same date, called Candlemas Day.

The Black-tailed Prairie Dog (*Cyonomys ludovicianus*) is not a dog, but a stout, short-legged, burrowing squirrel, which lives in the plains and plateaus of the Dakotas, south through New Mexico and Arizona. It is about 11 to 13 inches long and has a 4-inch tail. The fur is reddish-brown above and buff-tinged with brown below. Prairie dogs live in colonies or "towns," containing thousands of individuals. A prairie dog town is organized into wards along topographic lines. Each ward contains several, sometimes hundreds, of coteries, each headed by a male who has

won his place by fighting. His entourage consists of 1 to 4 females and the young of the past two years. The individual burrows are highly complex and have a mound of earth 2 or 3 feet high encircling the entrance to keep out surface water. Here the prairie dog sits upright as a sentinel. If danger appears it gives the alarm, a sort of sharp "yap"—hence the name prairie dog. There are various alarm calls, depending on the type of threat. If it seems serious it pops into its hole. It may live to be 10 years old. In the spring the female bears a litter of five naked, blind young in a grass-lined nest in a side burrow of the tunnel.

Ground Squirrels (*Citellus*) are generally fatter, shorter-legged and shorter-tailed than their tree-dwelling cousins. But they are not as stocky as the marmots, which also are ground-dwelling squirrels. *Citellus* comprises 14 species in the western United States and Canada and seven species living in eastern Europe and central Asia. They prefer arid prairies or rocky areas. They are able to climb, but prefer to remain on the ground, and are fond of light and sun. They are vigorous diggers and most are social animals which live in complex underground squirrel towns. They hibernate much of the year, sometimes from August to February. Their diet consists of seeds, plants and insects. Within a month of their birth the young, who are born blind, become independent. In some species the one yearly litter may include as many as 13. Ground squirrels often damage crops and pastures by devouring the vegetation and churning up the soil.

Richardson's Ground Squirrel (*Citellus richardsonii*) is found from Minnesota westwards in prairies and meadows. It is 8 to 9½ inches long, with a 4½-inch tail. Its fur is dull gray above and paler below. The tail is usually light brown. It has a shrill birdlike voice.

Castoridae, *the beaver (above), has a broad, flat tail which acts as a rudder when swimming. The tail is designed to turn at an angle, allowing the beaver, when he is transporting logs, to maintain a straight course.*

The colored area on the map shows the distribution of Geomyidae, or pocket gophers.

The Spotted Ground Squirrel (*Citellus spilosoma*) is the only spotted ground squirrel in the United States and Mexico. It is 8½ inches long including the 3-inch tail. It is grayish- or reddish-brown with light, square-shaped spots on the back. Living in semiarid plains, it eats seeds and insects. European species of the ground squirrel include *Citellus citellus* and *C. suslicus.*

The Thirteen-lined Ground Squirrel (*Citellus tridecemlineatus*) has a really remarkable coat. Not only is it adorned with handsome dark brown stripes, but each stripe is decorated with a row of white dots or "stars." It varies its vegetarian diet with grasshoppers, insects, field mice and birds' eggs, when it can get them. It is fairly common on the western prairies, but it is shy.

The Eastern Chipmunk (*Tamias striatus*) is the only American squirrel with face stripes. Its head and body are 5 to 6 inches long, and its tail is 4 inches. Its head is disproportionately large—and so are its cheek pouches. When they are full with a load of seeds on

The kangaroo rat (above) digs burrows in the arid or semiarid regions of North America, where it stores food.

their way to the storehouse, each may swell to the size of the head itself, presenting a startling appearance. It is reddish-brown above and white below. The Eastern chipmunk lives in hardwood forests. Its diet consists of acorns, nuts, wheat and corn. There are usually two litters a year. The three to eight young are born in an underground chamber and live to be about eight years of age. The eastern chipmunk's call is a clear, repeated "chip."

The Southern Flying Squirrel (*Glaucomys volans*) is common throughout the eastern United States. Another slightly larger species, the Northern Flying Squirrel (*G. sabrinus*) is found in the wooded areas of Canada, and from southern Alaska south through California, Utah and Wyoming. *G. volans* is about 10 inches long with a 6-inch tail. It is incredibly agile and sure-footed. A flying squirrel will gallop up a tree and leap out into the air, with arms and legs spread wide.

The beaver (right) dries its thick, waterproof coat simply by shaking the water from it.

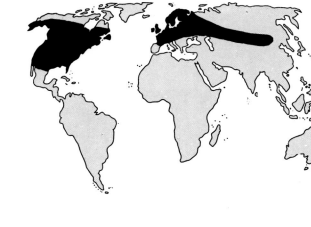

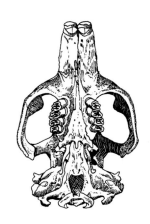

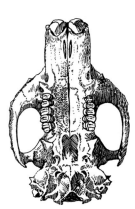

The skull of the marmot (top) and of the beaver (bottom) show the typical dentition of rodents. The beaver, however, has larger incisors and stronger cheek arches.

The distribution of Castoridae, as indicated by the colored areas on the map, includes North America, northern Europe and central Asia.

88

The furry flying membrane stretches from wrist to ankle, and with skillful manipulation of the wrists and tail the squirrel guides itself to the trunk of another tree. There at the last second the tail flips up and the arms and legs swing forward, forming a sort of parachute air brake. The squirrel lands upright on the tree and instantly runs around to the other side, just in case an owl or other predator has followed its flight.

The flying squirrel's way of life is much like that of other tree squirrels, except that it is active only at night. During the day it sleeps in its nest hidden away in a tree hollow.

Twelve other genera of flying squirrels live for the most part in China, southeast Asia, Sumatra and Borneo. One genus, *Petaurista*, contains giants with head and body lengths of up to 2 feet, and a tail of equal length. In contrast, *Petaurillus* of Borneo is a 3-inch pygmy.

The beaver's lodge (below) contains a one-room apartment just above water level. These living quarters are kept in good repair and last for many years.

The springhare (Pedetidae) has the appearance of a small kangaroo. Its hind legs are long and very powerful.

Geomyidae— The Pocket Gophers

These unsocial, rarely seen mammals are toothy, chunky and big-headed. They are brownish and rat-sized, ranging in length from 4 to 10 inches not including the tail. Pocket gophers are noted for their fur-lined cheek pouches, which are used to carry food. Their sturdy, long-clawed feet are well adapted for fast digging. The eyes and ears are small, and the incisors close outside the lips. This feature allows the animal to cut roots and pry away pebbles without swallowing too much dirt. They spend almost all of their lives underground in a maze of burrows containing the nest, storage chambers and even a toilet chamber. The gopher's diet consists mostly of roots and bulbs, and although it often damages crops, it helps to keep the soil fertile and porous. The one to five young are born after a gestation period of about 28 days, usually one to three times a year. This family includes about eight genera and about 30 species found only in North America from Canada to Panama.

The Heteromyidae (pocket mice, kangaroo mice and kangaroo rats) include about 5 genera and 70 species equipped with external fur-lined cheek pouches similar to the pocket gopher. The head and body length is 2 to 7 inches. They are long-tailed, nocturnal, burrowing rodents which inhabit the arid or semi arid plains and prairies. They are active at night and usually plug the tunnel entrances during the day. Their principal foods are seeds and greens. They do not drink water, but get it from the greens and by metabolic conversion of the seeds into water. The one to eight young are born in the spring and summer; there are one or more litters a year. Their range is the western United States, southward to Colombia and Venezuela.

Kangaroo Mice (*Microdipodops megacephalus*) are aptly named—they look and hop just like tiny kangaroos. A kangaroo mouse is less than three inches long, plus a long tail in which fat is stored for lean times. They may be seen around shrubs in arid regions of Oregon, Nevada and Utah. They never drink water, getting all they need as their diet of seeds is metabolized in the body.

Kangaroo Rats (*Dipodomys phillipsii*) are somewhat larger, reaching a length of 7 inches plus an equal-length tail. Twenty-two species range from the Missouri River southwest to central Mexico. They emerge from their burrows only at night to feed on seeds, leaves and buds and to stuff their cheek pouches with food to be carried back to the burrow and stored against lean times.

Castoridae—The Beavers

This family contains only one genus and two very similar species, found in northern North America and northern Europe.

The beaver is one of the largest rodents. It continues to grow throughout its life. A 15-year-old beaver may reach a length of more than 3 feet, plus a foot-long tail, and weigh 50 pounds. The body is stocky, and the limbs are short, with long curved and webbed digits ideally adapted to digging and swimming. The thick fur for which the beaver is hunted extensively is chestnut brown and

The black-bellied hamster, Cricetus cricetus, has large cheek pouches which it stuffs with huge quantities of grain to be transported to its burrow. When attacked, the hamster will blow the contents of its cheek pouches in the face of the enemy with surprising force.

The colored areas of the map represent the almost worldwide distribution of Cricetidae.

waterproof. The beaver's sense of hearing is keen, although its ears are small. The incisors are strong, orange-colored and capable of gnawing through a tree 1½ feet in diameter. The mouth closes behind the incisors enabling the beaver to work with its teeth underwater. These teeth are so sharp that the Indians used them for scalpels. The beaver has a flat, scaly tail, which functions as a rudder and as a support on land when the beaver rears on its hind legs to fell trees. When alarmed, it slaps this tail against the water as a warning signal, then dives. A beaver

can stay underwater 15 minutes. The anal glands contain "castor," a musky substance which is deposited on stones and mud as recognition signals. Mating takes place in the last months of winter. The number of young is usually two to four, which stay with their parents for two years, and then are driven from their home lake to fend for themselves. The beaver is or has been forced to become a nocturnal creature. It feeds on aquatic plants, young shoots, leaves, roots and bark. It is the only mammal besides man which engineers changes in its environment to suit its needs. Beavers build and maintain dams in streams to raise the water to a desired level. The dams are built on a foundation of stones and are made of tree branches cut into appropriate lengths with twigs, leaves and mud caulking the interstices. An ordinary dam may be 200 feet long and 5 feet high. In a like manner the beaver builds a lodge, roughly conical, with an underwater entrance and a nest above the water line. Then it cuts and anchors a huge pile of green branches, the bark to be used as food during the winter. As the supply of nearby trees is consumed, it digs long canals; tree sections can then be floated rather than dragged to the lake.

Impressive as the modern beaver is, it pales beside its recent ancestors. Several thousand years ago, beavers as big as half-grown bears inhabited the American West.

Pedetidae—The Springhares

This family has one genus and two species. The animals are remarkable because they resemble mice in the snout, rabbits in the ears, squirrels in the shape of their trunk and tail, and kangaroos generally. The springhare (*Pedetes capensis*) is 16 to 20 inches long, with an equally long black-tipped tail. It gets about by hopping on all fours like a rabbit; when frightened it leaps like a kangaroo. It can easily make 9 feet at a hop. The long fur, thick and soft, is reddish-brown with touches of white above and below. Springhares dig complex burrows in which the female bears one or two young during the summer. The animal is indigenous to South Africa, Kenya and Angola and is considered a pest by farmers.

Cricetidae— From Rats to Gerbils

This family of rodents is enormous—100 genera with some 720 species are found worldwide, except for Australia, Iceland and

Ireland. Most Cricetidae are small, with short bodies and limbs and rounded noses. They have 16 teeth: $I\ ^{1/1}$, $C\ ^{0/0}$, $Pm\ ^{0/0}$, $M\ ^{3/3}$. Fossils of this family date back about 25,000,000 years to the Oligocene period. To describe all the genera alone would take a whole book. The following, therefore, is a sampling which gives a fair cross-section of this family.

The Rice Rats (*Oryzomys*) were so named because one species flourished in the once-extensive rice fields of the southern states. There are more than 100 species. The average length is 5 inches plus a 7-inch tail. Color ranges from gray through buff to russet. In marshy areas, a grassy nest is built high in reeds and bushes. In drier areas the nest is in a shallow burrow. At mating time the famale

Peromyscus, the white-footed mouse (far left), is a real musician. It makes a buzzing hum in its throat and a drumming sound by thumping its front feet against a brittle leaf.

The black-bellied hamster's markings (left and bottom) are a curious reversal of nature's usual color scheme. Most animals are dark above and paler below, but the hamster is light brown, red and white above with black underparts.

ranges out seeking a mate. Some 25 days later her family of four to five is born, and within a few hours she goes out again to find another male with whom to mate. The young are full grown at four months, although the female can breed at seven weeks.

The Neotropical Water Rats (*Nectomys*) live most often in the woodland near the water. Their overall length ranges from 12 to 20 inches, half of which is tail. A line of short, stiff hairs on the underside of the tail acts as a keel when swimming. Its partial adaptation to an aquatic life suggests it may be evolving in that direction. It is found in northern South America.

The American Harvest Mice (*Reithrodontomys*). The 16 species of this genus are often found in short grass areas, but it also lives in salty marshlands and tropical forests, even above the timber line in the mountains. It varies in length from 2 to 5½ inches, with a 3- to 4-inch tail. Its neat globular nests of grass 6 inches in diameter are built in the high grass or shrubs. Winter nests are usually in burrows. Adult mice apparently moult once a year. Its diet consists of seeds, green shoots and insects. It does not thrive on cultivated land.

The White-footed Mice (*Peromyscus*), also called the deer mice, range from Colombia northward to Alaska and Labrador, in almost every possible habitat. They are usually the most common mammal in their range. There are 55 species. Their length is 3 to 6 inches, plus a 2- to 8-inch tail. Their coloring is variable, from gray to reddish-brown above with a dorsal stripe, and white below. They often live in pairs, which is unusual for small mammals. Their food preferences are seeds, nuts, berries, fruits and insects, but may include carrion. Their nests are found in burrows, hollow logs or crevices of any kind. They often utter thin squeaks, or a buzzing hum, and thump their feet rapidly on a leaf or reed. Because they are clean, easily fed, and have a high reproduction rate, deer mice are used extensively in laboratory studies of physiology and genetics.

Grasshopper Mice (*Onychomys*) are sometimes called scorpion mice because they like to eat scorpions. These 5-inch mice will also eat any other small rodent that can be overpowered—a pocket mouse, for example—by leaping from ambush. The grasshopper mouse grabs the prey by the head, lays back its ears, closes its eyes and clamps down. Sometimes it will stand on its hind legs, point its nose to the sky and give forth a tiny "wolf call"—a full second, tiny and high-pitched, but smooth; a howl that can be heard 50 feet away. Its range is southern Canada to northern Mexico.

The Mole Rats or Rodent Moles (*Myospalax*) live underground in wooded areas, especially the valleys between mountains in central Russia, northern China and Siberia. The fur color ranges from gray to grayish-brown to a pink-tinged russet. They are built for digging and walk with their strong, thick front claws doubled under. Their eyes are no more than pinpoints set admist soft, furry hair.

The Pack Rat, Trade Rat, Wood Rat, Brush Rat, Cave Rat—call it what you will, it is still *Neotoma*. Twenty-two species inhabit western and southern North America south to Nicaragua. The name stems from their urge to collect bright objects—pebbles, coins, colored glass, bleached bones, false teeth, etc. Their nests are globular affairs made of grass, sticks and any other available substance. These are permanent homes and may tower 3 to 4 feet high. In arid areas the nests are built around spiny cacti. Dashing in among the needles, the rat feels secure from predators. Other favored sites are rock crannies and tree forks. A pack rat may steal a bright object from a campsite, leaving something in its place. This does not mean

The tunnels in the burrow of the sand rat Meriones libycus are excavated on two levels and connected to one another by steeply slanted passages. The diagram (below) is an actual plotting of such a burrow.

The meadow mouse or vole, Microtus (right) eats its own weight in seeds, leaves and grasses every 24 hours. This great appetite requires an almost constant search for food.

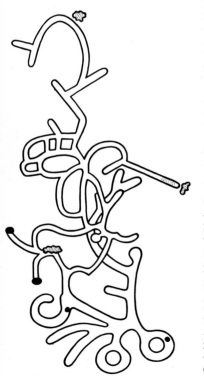

months and ready to reproduce. They usually live less than one year.

The Indian Bush Rat or Coffee Rat (*Golunda*) usually inhabits jungles, grasslands and swamps. This species did great damage to crops on plantations in Ceylon, by eating the buds and blossoms of the plants. Its diet usually consists of the roots and stems of most vegetation, especially the "dub" or "nariyali" grass indigenous to India. These rodents are good climbers and live either alone or in family groups.

The Thick-tailed Rat (*Zyzomys*) lives in the rocky hills and cliff areas of Australia. The fur is bristly. It is brown, gray, buff or reddish above and whitish below and on the hands and feet. These thin-skinned, delicately built animals have a long, brittle tail. The skin of the tail thickens gradually as the animal ages; thus the oldest rats usually have the thickest tails.

These brief descriptions of a few species chosen from the many possible are enough to show the tremendous distribution and variety of Muridae in the world. The genus *Rattus* alone embraces almost 570 species.

The colored areas of the map show the distribution of Gliridae, a family which includes dormice and hazel mice.

It is fruitless to venture into the labyrinth of such a multiplicity of forms. But two species, the black rat (*Rattus rattus*) and the Norway rat (*Rattus norvegicus*), are so widespread and common that they are of huge economic importance.

Neither species originated in Europe; both immigrated from Asia. The black rat entered Europe in the 12th or 13th century on the ships of the returning Crusaders The Norway rat was first seen in Europe in 1553, and was introduced into North America in about 1775. Both species are known to harbor and carry such diseases as rabies, trichinosis, typhus, salmonella food poisoning

Dormice (Muscardinus is shown on the opposite page) inhabit the thickets and forests of Europe and Asia Minor. They are agile climbers, but are active usually only at night. During the day they sleep in well-made nests firmly attached to the lower branches. They are dormant from October until April. During this time they lie curled in a ground nest, usually located under leaves or in a stump. In their deepest winter sleep their blood temperature may fall to a fraction of a degree above freezing.

These drawings compare the molars of the edible dormouse (left) and the common dormouse (right). Both are members of the Gliridae family.

The edible dormouse (Glis glis), a nocturnal animal, sleeps during the day in its home in a hollow tree. (opposite page and far left)

and bubonic (black) plague, which on several occasions has killed more than one quarter of the people in Europe.

The Black Rat (*Rattus rattus*) is most widely distributed in southern Europe and North Africa. Weighing less than a pound, it is the common house rat of the Mediterranean region, the southern United States, and Central and South America. Omnivorous and insatiable, it follows wherever man goes, invading his food supplies, chewing insulation

The hazel mouse Muscardinus avellanarius (below) derives its name from its strong passion for hazel nuts. It does not crack the nut, but gnaws a hole and removes the meat in small pieces.

off wires and even gnawing through lead drain pipes. Behind walls and under streets black rats construct lairs lined with soft material. As many as twelve times a year the female gives birth to five to twelve young. In three months they, too, are ready to breed.

The Norway Rat (*Rattus norvegicus*) is larger and fiercer than the black rat. Also known as the brown rat, gray rat, wharf rat and house rat, it gobbles every kind of food and will even eat its own kind. With its broad food tolerances and its ability to gnaw through any barrier it is perfectly equipped to thrive in man's habitations. It is known for its preference for cellars, stream banks and sewers. It is an animal capable of arousing fear in most cats. It bites babies in their sleep and is said to have gnawed the bellies of live swine. In man's terms it is a disaster, but in rat's terms it is one of the most successful of mammals. Man may wipe out the cheetah and the white rhinoceros, but the Norway rat will always be with us.

The House Mouse (*Musculus*) is 2½ to 4 inches long, with a tail of equal size; it is dark brownish-gray above and lighter gray below.

It is found in houses in the city and country; in the summer it can also be found in fields, near the woods and in the mountains. It eats virtually everything; it gnaws through furniture, fabrics and papers and uses these materials to upholster its nest. The female has four to six pregnancies a year, each producing four to eight young, which become independent within a month. The house mouse is a known carrier of typhus, spotted fever and other human diseases. All in all this tiny mouse is cute, but it is a pest. Innumerable

The Romans are said to have feasted on dormice. The mice were caught in the fall after they had fattened themselves for the winter. They were then kept in urns or other enclosures and fed acorns and chestnuts until the day of the feast.

Jaculus jaculus is the smallest of the desert jerboas, with a head and body length of about four inches, but its black-tufted tail with a white tip may be as long as 6 inches. Desert jerboas are social animals. Two or three may be found sleeping in the same nest, and they sometimes form loosely defined colonies.

The map shows the range of the family Dipodidae, which includes the jerboas.

A North American meadow jumping mouse nibbles a wild cherry, one of its favored foods. These mice also eat seeds, acorns and fungi, as well as insects and their larvae.

reports claim the house mouse can sing like a bird, but infinitely weaker. When experts examined a few singing mice, they discovered abnormalities in the nose and throat. The singing may have been nothing more than asthma.

Gliridae—The Dormice and Hazel Mice

Members of this family, which resemble small squirrels in habit and appearance, include seven genera and ten species. They are nocturnal, climbing animals which nest in hollow trees, among rocks, in the deserted burrows of other animals and in the attics of buildings. They fatten up in the fall, and then crawl into the nest and cover up the hole. They sleep from October until April. But weasels don't sleep in the winter, and many a dormouse never makes it to the spring. Their diet generally consists of fruit, nuts, insects and birds' eggs. They may seriously damage orchards by feeding on the ripening fruit. They are found in central and southern Europe east to Japan.

The Common Dormouse (*Glis glis*) is 6 to 7 inches long, with a 5- to 6-inch tail, and weighs about 6 ounces. Its thick, soft fur is brownish to silvery gray above and yellow to white below. The two to six young are born in a yearly litter.

Zapodidae—The Birch Mice and Jumping Mice

One species of this family, the North American Meadow jumping mouse (*Zapus hudsonius*), is about 4 inches long plus a 6½-inch tail. Its long, soft fur is yellowish-brown above and white below. It has powerful hind legs and gets about in a series of hops. When alarmed a jumping mouse can cover 12 feet in one bound, an amazing feat for a 1 ounce animal. It inhabits open fields, invades cultivated areas and builds outdoor nests for the summer, while its winter lethargy is spent in an underground den, with its muzzle against its belly and its long tail twined around its body.

Dipodidae—The Jerboas

Southwestern Asia and Africa are the homes for ten genera and 25 species. The jerboa has won man's admiration and attention for its abundant gracefulness since the days of ancient Egypt, when it was often included in paintings. Its head is round, and the ears and eyes are large. The powerful hind legs are four times longer than the forelegs. When a jerboa is in a hurry, it hops along at such a frantic pace, it seems not to touch the

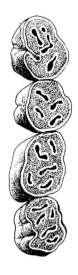

ground—as if it were in actual but erratic flight. Jerboas live in the semidesert areas, where the sandy soil is easily tunneled; they spend the day in the well lined den and search for buds, seeds, roots and insects at night. Jerboas do not require water in their diet when in the wild, but drink readily in captivity. They range in size from 1½ to 5 inches in length, with tufted tails almost twice as long as the head and body.

Hystricomorpha—
The Porcupines

The Hystricomorpha are divided into two families. Hystricidae, the Old World Porcupines, has four genera: *Thecurus, Hystrix, Atherurus,* and *Trichys,* with a total of about 20 species Erethizontidae, the New World Porcupines, also has four genera: *Erethizon, Coendou, Echinoprocta,* and *Choetomys,* with about 23 species.

Both families are large and stocky as rodents go and have coats studded with stout spines. They are vegetarian, mainly nocturnal, slow-moving and generally solitary. Old World porcupines do not climb trees. They nest in burrows either excavated by themselves or taken over from another burrowing animal, such as an aardvark. New World porcupines climb trees to get at bark and new shoots and do not burrow. They

The strong, solid teeth of the porcupine (above) are designed for efficient grinding of a wide variety of foods.

The map (right) shows the distribution of Hystricidae, the Old World porcupine.

make dens in rock crannies and under shrubs.

The Crested Porcupine (*Hystrix*) is the best known of the Old World porcupines. It has a squat, sturdy body and short legs, but the feet have strong claws suitable for digging. The bulky head has spiky whiskers, rather large eyes and small, round ears. Each foot has five digits but, especially in the forefoot, the thumb is rudimentary. The whole body is covered with rugged bristles. On the animal's back and haunches these are mixed with needle-sharp quills as long as 14 inches, and one-fifth of an inch in diameter; the tail, too, is studded with 2-inch quills, which are thin-walled and hollow. The animal's average length is about 2 feet, the tail is about 2½ inches long and the height at the shoulder is about 10 inches. The general coloration is dark brown. The animal derives a mottled appearance from the scattered whitish tint of its bristles and the tips and white rings of its quills. The muscles of the skin enable the porcupine to erect its quills. The animal prefers sunny, stony places with bushes. There it builds its den, adapting natural cavities to its use whenever possible. It is an ill-tempered creature. When threatened it attempts to run away in a clumsy gallop, but if pressed it will stop and raise its quills. It stamps its feet and vibrates the hollow quills of its tail, which produces a sound like a rattlesnake's rattle. It faces away from danger and may unexpectedly rush backward and attempt to impale the enemy. Men who chase them for sport or food have had their legs run through without quite knowing how it all happened.

The crested porcupine mates in the spring. Some four months later two young are born. Their eyes are open, their spines are well developed and they can walk. Ten days later the spines are already dangerous.

During the night these porcupines shuffle out of their den and forage for fruit, bark,

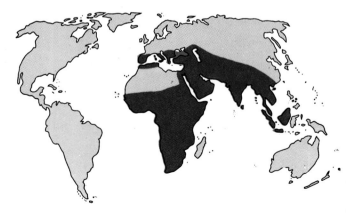

roots and tubers. By day they sleep in their dens. The crested porcupine is found in the Mediterranean area, especially North Africa, and along the lower Adriatic Sea.

An Indian species (*Hystrix leucura*) is about 28 inches long, and on the whole is lighter in color than the European species because it has more white in its bristles and quills. It lives in hilly regions and also on river banks, taking advantage of spaces among rocks as hiding places. It has powerful incisors with which it can gnaw through even the toughest wood or the ivory of elephant tusks. Otherwise it is not basically different from the European. Its habitat is the southern Himalayas, a large part of India, Ceylon, etc. Another species is exclusive to Africa: *H. africae-australis*, which ranges from South Africa to Ethiopia and Somalia.

The Brush-tailed Porcupine (*Atherus*) is about 18 inches long, plus 8 inches of tail. It is comparable to a fat rat with rough hair on its head, neck and lower areas, while on

The European porcupine (Hystrix) warns enemies by vibrating its long, hollow quills. If this rattle fails to deter the intruder, the porcupine will rush backward with quills raised and spear the attacker.

the back the bristles and quills become increasingly longer toward the tail until they reach about 4 inches. The tail itself ends in a tuft of long, rather scruffy bristles that look almost like small parchmented strips shredded at random. The animal's overall color is a yellowish-brown, lighter and almost white on the underparts. In its habits, it does not differ much from the common Old World porcupine. It inhabits woodlands of East Africa, central and southeast Asia.

The Long-tailed Porcupine (*Trichys*) is smaller—about 15 inches long, with a tail almost as long that has a plume of flat, stiff bristles at the tip. Otherwise it is generally similar to *Atherus*. Its habitat is the wooded plains area of Borneo, Sumatra and the Malaccan peninsula.

Among the New World porcupines the **North American Porcupine** (*Erethizon*) is the best known. It ranges in most of the forested areas of North America, except the southeast as far south as northern Mexico. Generally it grows to about 2 feet long, with a tail of 8 inches, but individuals with a head and body length of about 3 feet are encountered. A large male may weigh as much as 40 pounds, but the average is less than half that.

In contrast to the quills of the European porcupine, which are long and rapierlike, those of its American cousin are only 1 to 3 inches long—but they are fearsome weapons. There are 30,000 of them on the back, flanks and tail, loosely set and intricately barbed. The barbs are almost microscopic, and normally lie flat, but a few seconds after the quill enters flesh, they pop open, and the quill cannot be removed without ripping the flesh with it. Worse than that, the quills actually work themselves deeper at a slow but steady rate. Many is the animal that foolishly attacked a porcupine and died with quills penetrated deep into a vital organ. The porcupine's tactic is to hunch over with its back to a threat. Then when the predator sniffs cautiously, the porcupine lashes out with its quill-studded tail. Porcupines cannot shoot their quills; as folklore would have us believe, but the quills are so loosely attached that some of them fly off when the tail is swung.

For all its quite clumsy appearance, the porcupine is an excellent climber, using its claws, and it is an expert balancer even on fragile branches. It eats buds, tender shoots and green vegetation such as clover and alfalfa. It also shuffles along the ground, and it is quite a good swimmer, being buoyed up by its hollow quills. It is inordinately fond of salt and will eat ax handles, barn floors and posts, and even great slabs of plywood

The prehensile-tailed porcupine Coendou prehensilis *(below) is a lazy, slow-moving rodent, but an excellent climber. One reason for its climbing skill is its long, naked-tipped tail, which is used to grasp tree limbs and branches.*

to satisfy this craving. It mates in early winter and the birth, usually of one young, takes place about seven months later. It does not hibernate. When the snow is deep, the porcupine climbs trees and strips the bark from the upper branches.

Many of these details are applicable to the **Tree-dwelling Porcupines** (*Coendou*) of Central and northern South America. They are 12 to 24 inches long, with an equally long tail, bare for most of its length and prehensile. These nocturnal animals are brown with a tendency to russet or dark yellow; virtually the whole body is sprinkled with black, yellow and white spines varying in length with body areas and reaching a maximum of almost 5 inches in some species.

The map (left) shows the distribution of the family Erethizontidae, New World porcupines.

The 22 species of the genus Coendou *are easily tamed. Although they will fight enemies fiercely, they abandon their hostility soon after capture.*

The **Upper Amazon Porcupine or Andean Hedgehog** (*Echinoprocta*) lives in the equatorial forests of Ecuador and Colombia. It is less than 16 inches long, while its tail measures almost 5 inches. Its long hair is dark, ranging from gray to virtually black, and its quills (which are more numerous along the dorsal line and the top of the tail) are also dark, verging toward russet. Each foot has four digits with callous pads that are of great use to the animal on the ground and in trees. Another South American species, especially frequent in eastern Brazil, is the **Thin-spined Porcupine** (*Chaetomys*). Its muzzle is broad and flat and its color is dark. Like the other species, it has quills, but they are somewhat stiff only in certain areas (the top of the head, the neck, the shoulders, the base of the tail), while in other parts they seem almost to be thick, long, soft bristles. These animals reach lengths of 30 inches. A third of this is tail—which, however, is not prehensile. This is a rare species that lives on the ground, although it is capable of climbing trees.

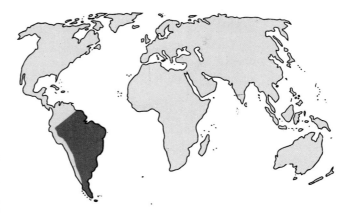

Cavididae—The Guinea Pigs or Cavies and Patagonian Hares

The Guinea Pig (*Cavia*) is the most docile animal imaginable, never aggressive, affectionate and of no great intelligence. It is so amenable that even a child can handle it without danger. Its long head terminates in an elongated muzzle; the eyes are quite lively, and the ears have well developed pavillions. The neck is not prominent but blends into the short, rotund body, which has short limbs and a stub of a tail. Length ranges from 8 to 12 inches. There are four digits on the front foot and three on the hind foot; and there are 20 teeth, arranged I $^{1/1}$, C $^{0/0}$, Pm $^{1/1}$, M $^{3/3}$; the incisors are rather short. In the wild, about 20 species are found in Colombia, Venezuela and Brazil, in rocky areas, savannahs and even swamps. Hair differs among the varieties that have been developed by breeders: rough, soft, short, long and very long (Angora). The range of colors, whether solid or mixed, is very broad. The guinea pig is exclusively vegetarian. It is bred for its meat, but above all it lends itself to laboratory use, because of its docility, its high rate of reproduction and early maturity.

The Patagonian Hare (*Dolichotis patagonum*) is about 20 inches long with a 2-inch tail. Its quick, sturdy body, strongest at the hind-

Dolichotis, *the Patagonian hare or "mara" (opposite page), has a form similar to the long-legged, long-eared Leporidae (hares and rabbits).*

The map indicates that the distribution of the family Caviidae, which includes guinea pigs or cavies, mocos and Patagonian hares or maras, is limited to South America.

A peculiar hopping gallop allows the Patagonian hare (Dolichotis patagona, left) to run at an incredibly high rate of speed.

er parts, is poised on long, slim legs that give the animal the appearance almost of a jackrabbit. This impression is heightened by the rounded ears, which measure almost 4 inches, and its cleft upper lip. The Patagonian hare usually eats herbs, roots and bark, sometimes invading cultivated fields for food and leaving damage behind. It often takes over other animals' dens as its own, for residence or for refuge, lining them with soft materials. It inhabits the broad plains of Argentina and Patagonia, where it is hunted for its flesh and for its skin, which is used to make blankets.

Hydrochoeridae— The Capybaras, Water Pigs

The Capybara (*Hydrochoerus*) is the only known representative of the family. It resembles the guinea pig but is remarkably large for the rodent order, as much as 4 feet long and 2 feet high at the shoulder. Occasionally it is even larger, and its weight can exceed 100 pounds. Very close relatives of this exceptional rodent have left fossil remains from the Pleistocene in North America, where the species no longer exists. Its chief characteristics are its short muzzle with a tremendous mouth, its very small eyes and ears, its four-toed forefeet and three-toed hind feet, and the massive squatness of all the parts of its body, beginning with the head and running through the neck to the trunk. There is no tail, and the legs are short. The incisors, which are visible through the cleft in the upper lip, are yellowish. The capybara, which is covered by a hairy coat ranging from brown to reddish-yellow, lives along the banks of streams and lakes, hiding among the lush vegetation. It swims and dives with ease and lives on aquatic plants when it can; it also invades sugar cane plantations. When contented capybaras emit low

Guinea pigs (Cavia) are native to central South America. In the wild they are rather coarse-haired and colored brown or gray. They are quite docile and do not bite. If they are kept warm and are given a reasonable amount of care they remain healthy and contented in captivity. Domestic breeds, such as those shown here, come in a variety of colors and patterns, and are frequently used in laboratory studies of disease, nutrition and heredity.

clicking sounds; sometimes they grunt like a pig. They are found from Panama to Rio de la Plata, and up the Amazon as far as Bolivia and Peru.

Dasyproctidae— The Pacas and Agoutis

These form a family of three genera and some 30 species in tropical America from central Mexico to southern Brazil. They have small piglike bodies and rabbitlike heads.

The Paca (*Cuniculus*) is a clumsy animal 2 feet or more in length, with a rudimentary tail and a broad head. It has marked cheek pouches and strong orange-colored incisors. A unique feature not found in any other mammal is the cheek bone or zygomatic arch, which is modified as a resonating chamber. Yet its voice when angered is just a low growl. The digits of each foot end in hooflike nails—four in front and five in back. Pacas dig dens more than 3 feet deep and spend the day there, alone or with a mate. They are active at night and in general feed on vegetable matter. The species is not very prolific; the female has a single birth in the summer. Its habitat is the marshy woods of a good part of South America, especially Brazil, Paraguay and the islands of Trinidad and Tobago in the southern Antilles. It is hunted for its flesh, which has been likened to pork.

The Agouti (*Dasyprocta*) has large eyes, rounded, short ears and a blunt muzzle with highly developed incisors that are red in the upper jaw and yellow in the lower. The hairs in its coat, which in some parts are almost 3 inches long, are variegated, assuming a changing color that ranges from light to dark brown to orange-yellow. It gives birth frequently, two to three young each time, and is quite prolific. It eats all kinds of vegetable matter and can do much damage to sugar cane. It is hunted fiercely and is prized for its flesh. It protects itself by "freezing" or by running with remarkable speed and agility. Its range is in forest land from southern Mexico to southern Brazil. Apparently it has been exterminated in the Antilles. Captured in its youth, the agouti can be easily domesticated, and is well known for its cleanliness.

Chinchillidae—The Viscachas and Chinchillas

The Pampas Viscacha (*Lagostomus maximus*) is the Argentine equivalent of the North American prairie dog. It has a large blunt head with prominent mustaches of drooping vibrissae and black and white stripes on the face. They live in colonies of 15 to 30 all across the pampas. Their warrens are an extensive network of tunnels which are sometimes shared with owls and snakes. Viscachas

The Patagonian cavy (Dolichotis) looks like a hare, with its long hind legs and ears, but is actually a rodent. The molars, shown in the drawing, have sharp enamel ridges, with each tooth showing an inverted S-shaped form.

are very clean, and the burrows are used for decades on end. All refuse is removed and piled around the entrance. In addition, stones, sticks, bones and any other object the viscacha can carry are added to the pile, apparently for decorative reasons. Viscachas consume range grass and their burrows are a threat to livestock. Consequently the Argentinians have been trying for 70 years to exterminate them.

The Chinchilla (*Chinchilla chinchilla*) lives in the cold and barren mountains of Chile and Peru at altitudes of up to 18,000 feet. No other mammal's fur is so costly or delicate. It is said that each individual hair is so fine that about 500 of them equal the thickness of a single human hair.

Such quality had already aroused the interest of the ancient Incas, who used the fur in the manufacture of materials of the greatest fineness and beauty In modern times, coats made of wild chinchilla have sold for as much as $100,000. The chinchilla has large, black eyes, rounded prominent ears, a short, squat body and small and delicate feet. Its

total length is about 13 inches, including the tail brush. Its splendid fur has hairs up to 2 inches long. It is a kind of gray-blue or dusky gray above and somewhat lighter below. The muzzle has long black whiskers. After a pregnancy of three or four months, the female gives birth in the summer to as many as four young. It lives in large families in a single den among the cliffs. Trade in chinchilla fur is now supplied almost exclusively by breeders, who find two related species particularly adapted to their work: the smaller *C. laniger* and the short-tailed chinchilla (*C. brevicaudata*) of Peru. Today the Chilean government protects the wild chinchilla, and it is coming back from a state of near depletion.

Capromyidae— The Hutias, or Nutrias

The West Indies are the remnants of an ancient, much larger land mass. Here a rich assortment of animals flourished—particularly rodents, some of which were huge. Today the

The pacarana or false paca, Dinomys branickii (below), moves with a slow, waddling gait which makes it easy prey for South American natives and other predators.

This drawing of the dental structure of the capybara shows the multiple folds in the enamel of the molars.

114

hutias are the only mammals native to the West Indies. Fossil evidence suggests they are the sole descendants of the ancient rodents.

The Cuban Hutia (*Capromys pilorides*) is about 2 feet long with a tail about a third as long. In general it looks like a large rat. The rather coarse coat ranges from buff to black. Another, smaller, Cuban species has a prehensile tail. Jamaica and the Bahamas are home to the **Short-tailed Hutia** (*Geocapromys*). It is about as big as a cottontail rabbit, but has short legs and is quite stout. The flesh is good to eat, and the natives hunt them for food.

The Nutria (*Myocaster*) is native to southern South America. Also called the coypu, it is extensively bred today for the fur trade, since it has a resemblance to the beaver. It has a heavy body and a large head; it may grow to be 2 feet long, with a 16-inch scaly tail. The forefoot has five toes with a very small thumb, and there is webbing on the four toes of the hind foot The fifth toe is free and probably used for grooming the coat. The nutria has strong incisors of orange tint on the forward side and a scanty dentition: $I\ 1/1$, $C\ 0/0$, $Pm\ 0/0$, $M\ 4/4$. A gland the size of a walnut beneath the male's tail secretes a very aromatic liquid, castoreum, that serves as a sexual signal. The nipples of the female are located high on her flanks, so that the babies can nurse while the mother swims. The animal is essentially aquatic, moving awkwardly on land; it builds riverbank dens more than 40 inches long and 2 feet in diameter, which it uses for sleeping as well as for deliveries, in which litters can run to nine or ten young. The newborn are at once introduced to the water by their mother, who swims with her brood on her back.

Ctenomidae— The Tuco-Tucos

This family has only one genus, *Ctetomys*. About 50 species have been named, although some of these may simply be local variants. They inhabit the plains and uplands of South America from Brazil to Tierra del Fuego.

The capybara (below and below left) is the largest rodent on earth. A big one can weigh 100 pounds and be as long as 4 feet. A native of South America, it is usually found near water.

The colored parts of the
map show the areas of
South and Central Amer-
ica inhabited by Echimyi-
dae.

The spiny rat (top)
is usually found in for-
ests near water. It has a
relatively weak link at
the fifth vertebra of the
tail, a safety device
which allows the tail to
come off when caught.

half the size of the second, with their squat
bodies and disproportionately large heads,
which are broad and blunt. The eyes and
ears are very small, and the nails are long.
These animal dig honeycomb burrows with
their protruding teeth and strong claws. Dirt
is swept out of the burrows with the fringe-
bristled hind feet.

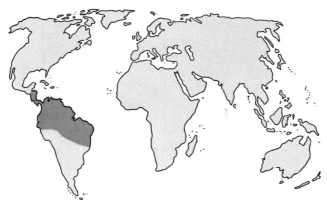

A totally different and unique aspect is
represented by the unadorned **Naked Mole
Rat** (*Heterocephalus*), which has only a
very few widely separated bristles growing
out of its wrinkled, pinkish, faded skin.
There are only a few tufts of hair, each including perhaps 10 bristles, on its muzzle; the
bristles scattered over the body are altogether
sporadic. The very tiny eyes seem incapable
of their job, and the small ears are practically
invisible. The mole rat spends its entire
life underground, burrowing to the surface
from time to time to kick out excavated dirt.

Ctenodactylidae— The Gundis and Speke's Pectinators

This is the last family among the rodents.
Its members, which resemble cavies with
large heads, have sharp-nailed toes with
comblike bristles on the two inner hind
digits for cleaning the fur. The tail is no

more than a stump; the squat body rests on short legs.

The Gundi (*Ctenodactylus*) is almost 8 inches long, plus its short tail. The thick, silky coat ranges from rust to gray. The gundi feeds on vegetables, which it also stores against periods of drought. Its habitat is northwest Africa.

In eastern Ethiopia and Somalia lives the related **Speke's Pectinator** (*Pectinator*) of approximately the same size. Its head and muzzle are reminiscent of the rabbit in the shape and mobility of the lips. There is something of the rabbit in its entire body too, with its short, hairy tail. Its color is a uniform gray, and it has long whiskers. Its cheeks seem to be puffed out, giving a roundish and pleased look to the muzzle. It is hunted as food and is regarded as a delicacy.

The nutria or coypu (above and left) looks like an otter. Its natural area is central and southern South America, but it has been introduced with great success to the United States and Europe for its fur-bearing qualities.

Thompson's gazelle (Gazella) ranges the grasslands and bush country of Kenya and Tanganyika. It is quite common and generally travels in small herds. The horizontal stripes on the face and flank are a distinguishing feature. The "Tommy" is a favorite prey of the cheetah, which can run it down with ease. About 25 species of gazelles inhabit central and northern Africa and Asia. The large, limpid eyes of these animals caused the Arabs to call them by the native term for "affectionate," from which the English name "gazelle" is derived.

Mammals—The Greatest Show on Earth

The five preceding books, and this book up to here, contain specific information about individual mammals—their various physical characteristics, habits and habitats. Each mammal is identified by its accepted scientific name. In this section, however, we propose to talk not of the properties that distinguish one mammal from another, but about the aspects they all share—those things that separate the mammals from all other living beings.

A masked shrew weighs a tenth of an ounce and feeds on grubs and insects. An African elephant, eating grass and leaves, may reach such a size that just one canine tooth (or tusk) alone may weigh 30,000 times as much as the whole shrew. Yet the anatomy of the shrew and of the elephant, bone for bone, organ for organ, is fundamentally the same.

On the other hand, an alligator and an otter in superficial ways are alike. Both are air-breathing animals adapted for life in the water. Both are predators with a liking for fish. Both are medium-sized, have flattened heads, long tapering tails, short legs and webbed feet which are employed while swimming. And when they want real speed, otter and alligator alike propel themselves with powerful undulations of the whole body.

But the American alligator lives only in the warmest parts of the country, whereas otters are widely distributed throughout the continent. In Canada an otter thinks nothing of chewing a hole through thick river ice and plunging in.

The obvious answer, of course, is that the otter has a warm fur coat, but even if we were to propose the ludicrous idea of applying a sleek furry coat to the alligator, it still could not survive freezing weather.

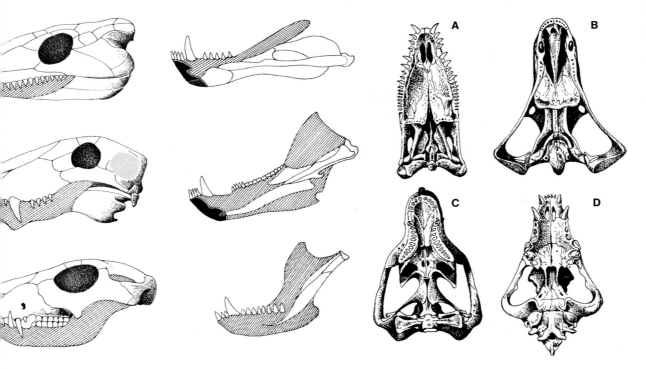

Generally a mammal is defined as an animal which (a) has hair for insulation or protection, (b) bears live young which had been nourished by a placenta in the mother's womb, (c) nurses the young by means of nipples, and (d) is warm-blooded—that is, it maintains a constant temperature regardless of the heat or chill of its environment. Mostly these things are true. But whales and elephants have no hair to speak of. Kangaroos have no placenta, and the baby 'roo is only a nub half an inch long at birth. Echidnas have no nipples; the milk simply oozes from many glands. A camel may have a blood temperature drop of 11 degrees between the hottest time of day and a cold night, and the temperature of a hibernating bat may drop to the low 40s. To make things more complicated, many nonmammals seem to act like mammals. Sharks bear live young. Eagles care for and train their eaglets in a most affectionate manner. And birds are just as warm-blooded as any mammal. In the animal world generalizations always seem to get tripped up by the example of a strange beast which has made a bizarre adjustment to assure its survival.

Mammals evolved from reptiles. This branching began 250 million years ago in Permian times, when reptiles themselves had yet to reach their peak. These first beasts in the line of mammals were more reptile than mammal, and until the age of the dinosaurs began 50 million years later, they were the dominant form of life. Then for 80 million years the dinosaurs—starting out as ostrich-sized animals—ruled the earth. Toward the middle of this time, in the Jurassic, real mammals appeared in the world. For the most part they were rat-sized, but for 40 million years these hairy, energetic, nibbling little beasts shared the earth with the 50-ton *Brachiosaurus*, the 20-foot-high *Tyrannosaurus* and hundreds of other types of dinosaurs which together formed the most bizarre assortment of animals the world has

These skeletons, from top to bottom, of Trinaxodon, Diademodon *(cynodonts of the Triassic period) and a modern primitive mammal (the tupaia) show the changes in the rib cage, which became shorter as time went on. This allows the lungs to expand toward the belly area.*

The pangolin (below) is a most unusual mammal. Although it has a few hairs here and there, its body is completely covered with hornlike scales. This is an extreme case of evolutionary adaptation to the environment.

A flying lemur (opposite page) is not a lemur at all, but of a separate order, Dermoptera. *It glides by means of a large membrane stretched between all four limbs. Here the folded membrane forms a cradle for a young one.*

ever seen. By Paleocene times, 55 million years ago, the dinosaurs had all died out, and the little mammals had most of the world to themselves.

Evolution occurs in fits and starts, not neat and in a straight line. Extinction is the rule, and survival is the wildest improbability. Yet as one type gets a foothold in the scheme of things, flourishes for a while, and then goes out, another rises to take its place.

Today practically every possible niche in the higher levels of the ecology is occupied by one or another kind of mammal. They are the undisputed masters of the earth. And this mastery results not from single details such as skin covering, but from an entire and vastly improved system for converting oxygen and food into energy and heat.

A typical reptile eats a limited amount of food in respect to its size, or if like the snake it eats a large quantity at a time, these occasions are spaced several days apart, and digestion is very slow. Moreover such animals can tolerate long fasts. Since its body temperature is little higher than that surrounding it a reptile has little requirement for calories beyond what it needs for muscle function. At low temperatures the reptile simply becomes torpid, stops feeding and fails to respond to stimuli.

Matters are very different with mammals. They ingest large amounts of food—the smaller the animal the larger the relative intake—which is actively chewed, or at least cut into bite-size chunks, and mixed with salivary and gastric juices to accelerate digestion.

The rapid and continually active metabolism of mammals, as compared to the slow and varied metabolism of reptiles, is made possible only by generally more efficient methods of eating, digesting, breathing, blood circulation and internal heat control.

The mouth, first of all, is very efficient. Instead of the peglike teeth of the reptile

which are used simply for grabbing and holding, the typical mammal has several types of well rooted teeth. In front there are the incisors, and these come in all sizes. In carnivores they are used for nipping. With these teeth a wolf can clean the last shred of meat from a bone. Rodents, of course, use them for gnawing and can cut through the hardest nutshell in seconds. In the case of grazing animals, strong fleshy lips come into play. They gather grass and leaves into bunches ready for the incisors to snatch off.

Although some mammals, such as baleen whales, do not chew at all, there is no doubt that mastication of food is an activity restricted to mammals. The canine teeth grab the food, and the molars and premolars chew it up. To aid in this action, mammals have a muscular tongue which works against a long bony palate to move the food from side to side and hold it in proper position for chewing. Behind the hard palate is the soft palate, which keeps the food out of the nasal passages, and allows the animal to breathe while chewing or gnawing. This need arises from the high rate of oxygen consumption and carbon monoxide discharge, which does not permit prolonged suspension of breathing.

Another fundamental characteristic of mammals is the clear division of the trunk into chest and abdominal regions. The divider is the diaphragm, a muscular septum that plays a great part in mammal respiration. In legged reptiles the ribs occupy the whole space between the shoulder girdle and the pelvis. Breathing is accomplished (except in turtles) by rotating the ribs forward and outward, which increases the volume within the rib cage. But in mammals the ribs extend only over the chest section. The soft belly area, not being enclosed, is allowed a limited movement. When the dome-shaped diaphragm contracts it flattens and pulls downward, expanding the lungs. The effect can be observed in a panting dog. As its

The African elephant is the largest and most powerful land animal alive in the world today. Elephants fear no other animal, and their only enemy is man. The hide is gray, tough and an inch thick. It has no hair to speak of—only thinly distributed bristles. Despite its thick hide, the elephant is quite sensitive to cold, and a light frost will give it severe cramps. The trunk is a marvelous example of adaptation. Actually just an overgrown nose and upper lip, it is a universal tool. With it the elephant can drag a two-ton log or shell a tiny peanut.

An African mole rat is tiny, almost blind and not nearly so intelligent as an elephant. Yet it is just as successful in its own way, and probably will still be thriving when the last African elephant is gone.

127

beaver may look sopping wet, but under the dense underfur it is dry and cozy.

To maintain a proper temperature a mammal must not only stay warm, but avoid overheating. This is accomplished by controlled evaporation. Sweat glands, liberally distributed in the skin, begin to function as soon as the body temperature tends to rise above normal. Such a rise could result from exposure to the summer sun or from the heat generated by exertion. Copious sweating, however, is restricted to those mammals that have only light coats of hair, or practically none at all, such as humans. Sweating is useless in animals with dense fur or wool, so they get along by panting. Rapidly moving air cools the wet surface of the tongue by evaporation. Blood, cooled by passage through the packed capillaries of the tongue, is then circulated throughout the rest of the

The leopard is a crafty predator which depends solely on herbivores, usually antelopes, for its food.

body. Similar action takes place in the lung passages. Many of the smaller desert mammals, like the reptiles, avoid the problem entirely by spending their days underground in cool burrows and coming out only at night. The hippopotamus has a special problem because it has a sensitive skin and almost no hair. It is too big to burrow so it must spend most of the day completely submerged or it will suffer from heat exhaustion. If its river dries up it dies.

No one knows whether hair first appeared as fuzz or as specialized bristles possibly used as feelers. But the front portion of a fossil skull of a therapsid—a mammallike reptile that lived during the middle Triassic period about 180 million years ago—shows furrows and indications of blood vessels that suggest the animal possessed specialized hairs and oil glands alongside the muzzle.

The 200 pound wart hog is a herbivore, but nevertheless tough. With its strong, hooked, foot-long tusks and aggressive disposition it can defend itself against most predators.

The dietary habits of a variety of rodents are shown on these pages. At right, a marmot nibbles on a berry. Below, a common dormouse sleeps amidst a litter of acorn shells; at bottom, a red squirrel cracks a nut. The chipmunk at bottom right will soon feast on strawberries. The hazel mouse at top left on the opposite page prefers hazel nuts; the two red squirrels to the right, like the ground squirrel at bottom, are all nut eaters. The marmot at far right has an overripe apple.

Beyond this, just how and when hair appeared is anybody's guess.

The high development of the brain is another general characteristic of mammals. The most stupid mammal is a genius in contrast to the most intelligent reptile, and the intelligence of mammals has far greater flexibility even than that of birds, though birds have very complex instinctual behavior patterns.

Mammals have a highly developed cerebral cortex—the surface layers of the two brain hemispheres where learning and rational thought take place. In the more advanced mammals this is deeply convoluted to increase the area. This part of the brain is small and smooth in reptiles, and the portions that deal with instinct and automatic reaction are dominant.

Mammals generally bear their young live and in an advanced state of development, whereas reptiles lay eggs. During the time the baby reptiles are growing inside the incubating egg they are subject to all sorts of threats. Other animals dig them up and eat them. Severe temperature changes may kill them. And when the young finally breaks out of the egg it is quite vulnerable, and indeed may even be eaten by its own mother or father. It must get along from the first minute by instinct and luck.

By contrast the young mammal is well protected inside its mother's womb, and after birth the mother continues to care for it and protect it, frequently to the point where she will fight savagely anything that threatens her baby.

She feeds it with rich milk from her breasts until it is strong enough to eat whatever food is proper to its kind—insects, fish, meat, grass, leaves, bark. In many species,

The tiger at right hunts under the cover of darkness and rests during the day. It may feast repeatedly on a large kill, which it keeps hidden. The tiger's black, white and tan stripes are excellent camouflage in the light and dark shadows cast by tall grass or woodland trees. It is an expert jumper, climber and swimmer.

The wolf (opposite page) has favorite hunting territories that may extend for 100 miles. Wolves will eat almost anything: domestic animals, large game, carrion and even berries and watermelon. A wolf pack consisting of about a dozen family members is able to kill a caribou or moose, but when the wolf is hungry it will settle for more meager meals, such as rabbits and rodents.

during this nursing period, the mother diligently cleans and grooms the youngster and teaches it the skills it will need to succeed on its own. There is no doubt that the comforting sensations of contact that nursing produces enhance the feelings of affection and protectiveness that the mother has for her young. In some cases, such as wolves, parental care and training are shared by the father, and even by an uncle or aunt who may be part of the group.

In the large grazing animals that travel in herds, training by the mother is least. The baby, usually one, is born at an advanced stage. Within a few minutes it is on its feet with its eyes wide open and ready to follow its mother.

The parents of one generation of a particular species never have exactly the same qualities or characteristics, aside from the fact that one is male and the other female, and the young are never just like their

parents, nor precisely like each other. Some may be slightly better suited for their particular mode of life than others. In a situation where big size is an advantage, the larger ones of each generation have a slightly better chance of living long enough to reproduce than their smaller brothers and sisters. In a hundred generations, then, a species may become measurably larger.

For example in Eocene times the ancestral horse *Eohippus,* no bigger than a fox terrier, lived in the forest, nibbling shoots and tender leaves. But the forests shrank and grassland spread. As conditions gradually changed, so did the horse. In the grasslands size and speed were the best protection against predators so the larger horses prevailed. Progress was not smooth, and the time span was long from the early horses to the present day. Fifty million years intervened—or to put it another way, about 15 million *generations* of horses have lived and adapted and died to produce the large, powerful and swift horses of today.

On the other hand some animals evolved very little down through the ages. Oysters, for instance, have shown almost no change at all for 200 million years. And the American opossum is much like its relatives of 80 million years ago when the last of the great dinosaurs still lived. Today's opossum is perhaps a bit larger, but otherwise is the same.

It has been a rough 100-million-year road that mammals have traveled. In the beginning the little mammals weren't too different from each other. Some, like the opossum, made the journey almost unchanged. Others branched off in the most surprisingly and unlikely directions. Many branches came to a dead end. But here we are today, an absolutely dumbfounding assortment of living mammals whose variety of size and color and proportion and function and simple beauty is a wonderful thing to behold.

A female cheetah rests in the grass with her two cubs. These animals usually form family groups of two or three adults with their young. Cheetahs are the fastest animals on land; from a resting position they can reach a speed of 45 miles per hour in two seconds. Several cheetahs have been clocked at 70 miles per hour, although their endurance is short: at top speeds, they become winded after 400-500 yards.

Perhaps the most splendid of all the mammals, the lion (Panthera leo) has been losing ground to the encroachment of civilization for many years. Unless a great effort is made to protect the lion, there is grave danger that even the King of Beasts will disappear from the face of the earth.

Index
Italicized page numbers refer to illustrations.